TALL TALES of
the Catskills

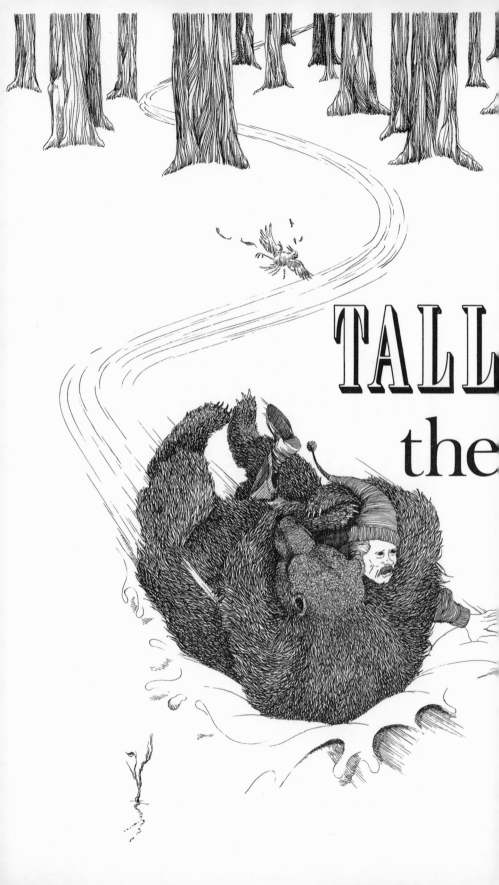

TALL
the

FRANK L. DU MOND

TALES of Catskills

drawings by Peter Parnall

ATHENEUM   New York   *1968*

COPYRIGHT © 1968 BY FRANK L. DU MOND
ALL RIGHTS RESERVED
LIBRARY OF CONGRESS CATALOG CARD NUMBER 68-18456
PUBLISHED SIMULTANEOUSLY IN CANADA BY
MCCLELLAND AND STEWART LTD.
MANUFACTURED IN THE UNITED STATES OF AMERICA BY
KINGSPORT PRESS, INC., KINGSPORT, TENNESSEE
DESIGNED BY JUDITH LERNER
FIRST EDITION

to my wife
MARGARET
with deep appreciation
for her constant encouragement
and helpful suggestions

Contents

TALL TALES of the Catskills

Foreword

OURS WAS A RAMBLING TWO-FAMILY HOUSE BUILT IN THE 1880's. We lived on on side, and my grandparents lived on the other side of the dividing wall. The only way to cross over was through a small doorway hidden near the bottom of the dark stairs that led to the second floor. Beyond that door was a narrow passage, that led between well-stocked pantry shelves. Every evening at the far end a wedge of soft light from a kerosene lamp marked a big comfortable kitchen with a warm-hearted wood stove. And there dwelt my grandmother, who served good things to eat, and my big, good-natured grandfather, who had a never-ending stock of fascinating tales of strange happenings in the Catskill Mountains when he was young . . . stories of bears, wolves, birds that laid square eggs, sidehill gougers, hoop-snakes, sweat fish, monstrous mosquitoes, and a sacred cherry-tree buck.

On our side of the double house I lived with my father, mother, brother and sister.

Papa—a country storekeeper, over six feet tall, slim as a rail, handlebar moustached—worked six days a week from seven in the morning until nine at night and then often opened up Sunday morning as a special favor to some neighbor who suddenly found that he had no tobacco to tide him over another day.

Mama—small, trim, sixty inches tall, with the appetite of a sparrow and the energy of a beaver—was a wonderful cook and housekeeper who kept the place as neat as a pin and could never rest if it was possible to find another speck of dirt.

My brother Clifford—not quite three years older than I—was big enough to help with the care of the delivery horses and to perform other duties around the store.

I was the middle one, and by 1905 I was able to open the pasture swinging gate and drive home Grandpa's cows at ten cents a week. On Saturday mornings I swept out Papa's store, for which I received my pay in penny candies. Occasionally I was made to feel important if some lady customer who liked children insisted that I wait on her and I had to struggle with the complicated operation of wrapping up a loaf of bread.

I was the shy, curly-haired one, small for my age and out-of-place playing with the big boys at such favorite country pastimes as tin can shinny in winter or duck-on-a-rock in summer. It was I that the teacher punished, to my great embarrassment, by making me sit on her lap, that the belligerent rooster attacked, that the neighbor's temperamental dog bit, and the trusted delivery horse ran away with.

The final member of the family was my sister Marion, thirteen months younger than I, interested in music and in being a junior housekeeper.

With Papa busy at the store until my bedtime, Mama's household duties keeping her on the go until much later, with Clifford playing outdoors with the big boys, and Marion occupied with her daily piano practice of one hour after supper, I was the restless one. So on evenings when I didn't have homework to do or the weather was bad outside, Mama was glad to have me cross over to the other side of the house to visit Grandpa and Grandma until time to go to bed. And I came to look upon my grandfather as a delightful source of evening entertainment, of stories told so believably that I was sure he was letting me in on special secrets he had hoarded for many years.

Treed by Wolves

NOT EVERY BOY HAS A BACK DOOR TO HIS GRANDMOTHER'S pantry and his grandfather's stories.

The memory of a discovery I had made and the prospect of one of Grandpa's tall tales drew me irresistably one night through the pantry back door to the other side of our two-family house to visit with my grandparents before going to bed.

Grandma sat at the kitchen table darning socks. Grandpa was smoking his pipe and reading the *Kingston Daily Freeman*.

"Come in, Frank," they said in unison.

"We hoped you'd come along and brighten up our evening," continued Grandma. "What did you do today after school?"

"Mart Stover and I played in his father's barn. Guess what we found in a barrel back in a corner?"

"A hen's nest," said Grandma.

"A litter of kittens," volunteered Grandpa.

"Nope. You're both wrong. Four big animal skins with their bushy tails still on 'em. They were sewed together on a blanket. Mart's mother thought they might be wolf skins."

6

Grandpa laid down his paper and removed his metal-rimmed spectacles. "Oh yes! I remember them. They're wolf skins, all right. Mart's great-grandfather was old Doctor Smith. He left to help our wounded boys in the Civil War and never came back. That's the lap robe he used in his cutter when he visited sick people around here in the wintertime many years ago."

"Did you ever see a wolf, Grandpa?"

"I saw lots of them when I was young. They were smart animals, smart enough to make a fool out of me."

"How could they do that?"

But before he could get another word in, Grandma spoke up: "While your grandfather is spinning his yarn, you might as well enjoy a treat I have for you." She got up and headed for the pantry.

Grandpa leaned back in his armchair and thoughtfully stroked his chin-whiskers. As he leisurely puffed on his clay pipe, his gaze followed the fragrant smoke as it slowly rose toward the ceiling and disappeared.

Grandma reappeared and set a glass of cider and one of her sugared doughnuts before me on the table. "All boys have hollow legs."

She turned toward Grandpa. "Now Abe, that you've had a chance to put on your thinking cap, I won't disturb you two again."

Grandpa smiled, hitched his chair closer to the table, put down his pipe, and began.

"One spring day when I was still living up in the hills with my folks I decided to look into the wild country on the other side of the mountain behind the farm for signs of beaver. Like all country boys I wanted to make some extra money by trapping. After a long, hard climb up the rocky slope and down the other side into territory I had never been in before, I saw below me a small stream winding its way through a narrow valley. Along its banks was a thick stand of aspen or poplar trees. This looked like beaver country.

"By this time I was tired, so I sat down to rest in a spot of sunlight with my back against a big pine tree. It was so quiet and peaceful that I had almost fallen asleep when a crow in the top of the tree gave a loud danger call. This was followed up by the chattering of a red squirrel in a nearby beech tree.

"I got up quietly and hid behind the tree. Bears, wolves, panthers and wildcats were still at home in the Catskills in those days. After a long tough winter they might be hungry and dangerous, and I had no gun.

"Looking carefully around I finally made out several gray timber wolves sneaking about in the undergrowth. They were big hungry-looking beasts.

"I seemed to be in the center of a circle they had made, and the circle was getting smaller. They were after me!

"A cold chill ran up my spine, and the hair on the back of my neck stood up. There wasn't a second to lose!

"The pine tree had no branches within reach. Quick as a flash I turned and raced toward the next tree, gave a mighty leap, grabbed the lowest branch and swung myself up just in time to escape the hungry jaws that snapped shut a few inches from my legs. I climbed higher as fast as I could so they couldn't possibly reach me. Then I looked down. There were six of them—an old pair and four almost full-grown young."

"Golly, Grandpa, what did you do then?"

"There wasn't anything I could do except make myself as comfortable as possible among the branches and wait for them to go away. But they didn't. They just sat there on the ground in a circle about the tree looking hungrily up at me.

"After a long time they got restless and began to pace back and forth and finally went into a huddle. Putting their heads together for a few minutes, they seemed to have decided what to do next. Four of them stayed on guard while the other two went trotting down the hillside and out of sight.

"What could they be up to? I got an uneasy feeling in the middle of my stomach.

"After a while I heard the sounds of snarling and grunting on the ground below. Looking down through the branches I saw that the two wolves that had gone away were coming back up the slope slowly herding a brown, short-legged animal in front of them. It was shuffling along just ahead of jaws that were snapping close to its rear. As it came closer I could see that it was a big beaver, so winded from its uphill walk that its lips were parted, showing a set of large, yellow, chisel-like front teeth."

"What was the beaver doing out there in the woods, Grandpa?"

"There must have been a beaver pond along the stream at the bottom of the hill. Beavers usually work only at night, but this was springtime and they were probably short of food. I guess the two wolves surprised this one busy felling a tree for the family food supply. Instead of killing it on the spot they drove it back up the hill to the rest of the pack.

"When the beaver reached the base of the tree where I was perched, all of the wolves went up to it and began to snarl and bare their wicked-looking teeth, but they didn't bite. The frightened animal, knowing it couldn't escape, took the hint. Sitting up, it began to gnaw into the tree trunk. The wolves became quiet and sat down to watch.

"As I saw the beaver cutting out a big chip of wood at every bite, I knew I was in real trouble. At the rate it was working it wouldn't be long before the tree would be cut down. So I moved lower among the branches, shouting at the top of my lungs in an effort to frighten the beaver away; but the wolves hemmed it in so it kept on cutting.

"Finally the tree began to tremble and lean to one side. With a crackling noise it leaned farther and farther until it began to fall. I closed my eyes and hung on for dear life thinking it would be better to be crushed to death under the tons of falling branches than to drop to the ground and be torn to pieces by the hungry wolves.

"Suddenly the downward motion stopped so quickly I almost lost my hold. Opening my eyes I was surprised to see that the tree had not fallen to the ground. The beaver, whether accidentally or purposely I didn't know, had felled the tree so it lodged on a slant against another tree standing next to it.

The disappointed wolves howled, but they didn't give up. Instead, they surrounded the beaver again and drove it over to the second tree, into which I had now climbed. Here the tired beaver began all over again, while I yelled and broke off dead branches and dropped them down in an effort to delay the awful fate that was ahead of me. But this had no effect, and the beaver kept working away until the second tree was about to fall.

"Then a shot rang out and five of the wolves took to their heels and disappeared from sight. The sixth lay stretched out on the ground, dead."

"What happened, Grandpa?"

"A mountaineer who happened to be hunting in the area heard my shouting and ran over to see what was going on. Taking in the situation at a glance, he shot one of the wolves and I was saved."

"You were pretty lucky. I was afraid they were going to get you that time."

"Yes, I was lucky. I climbed down shaking like a leaf."

"What happened to the beaver?"

"That tired old beaver just sat there with its lips parted in a big grin. After thanking the man for what he had done, I went over and gave the beaver a friendly pat on the head and it turned away and slowly ambled down the slope to the safety of the pond.

"And do you know, from that time on, to show my thankfulness, I never again set my traps for beaver or complained if they cut my trees or flooded my land with their ponds. To this day I do believe that smart old beaver purposely cut that first tree so it fell into the next one and in that way saved my life."

With the story ended, Grandma looked up and broke the spell: "Abe, you two are having such a good time I hate to tell you it's late and your grandson should be in bed. It's a good thing we live under one roof so all he has to do is to go back through the pantry and up the stairs."

"I suppose you're right, Liza. His folks won't let him come in to see us nights if he stays up too late."

I jumped up. I didn't dare run the risk of our story time being stopped.

"Thank you for the story, Grandpa. I liked it. And thank you, Grandma, for the cider and doughnut. Goodnight!"

There was a twinkle in Grandpa's eyes: "Goodnight, sleep tight and don't let the bugs bite! Next time I'll tell you how I used to shuck wolves."

Wolf-shucking

SEVERAL EVENINGS LATER FOUND ME HEADING BACK through the pantry to Grandma's kitchen to hear the story that had been promised.

Grandpa, who was sitting at the table reading his paper, looked up, smiled and nodded.

Grandma was ironing near the stove. The shiny tin reflector on the kerosene lamp in the bracket on the wall flooded her ironing board with cheerful light.

"You're just in time, Frank. While your grandfather is finishing his reading, you can put some wood in the stove for me. My new irons aren't hot enough to smooth out the wrinkles."

With the lifter I slid the front lid to one side and laid several sticks of seasoned oak onto the bed of glowing coals and put the lid back in place.

"There, Grandma, you'll have a good hot fire in a few minutes."

"Thank you! Your grandfather just bought me this nice set of flatirons, three different sizes with this detachable wooden handle, to make my ironing easier, but they won't do a good job if I don't keep them hot."

"Shall I push them farther back on the stove where

there is more heat?''

"Yes, that's good. Then while you're waiting, help yourself to a molasses cookie from the jar on the table. I baked them this afternoon, so they're fresh and chewy.''

Grandpa soon laid his paper aside, took off his specs and reached for his pipe. A few puffs later he was in the mood for another story.

"Let me see!'' he began. "You know, Frank, when I got back home that night after my narrow escape from the wolves, the more I thought of their cunning in getting the beaver to cut down the tree I had climbed, the madder I got. It hurt my pride as a woodsman to be outwitted by a pack of wild dogs.

"Then and there I swore I'd get even with the whole

wolf tribe if it was the last thing I ever did. But I wouldn't stoop to the ordinary everyday methods of shooting, trapping or poisoning them. I was much too peeved to use such common, old-fashioned ways of punishing the pesky critters. After giving it a lot of thought, I finally figured out an entirely new method of getting rid of them. I called it 'wolf-shucking'."

"What's wolf-shucking, Grandpa?"

"When you take the outside covering or shell off a hickory nut or a peanut, or even a clam, it's called shucking. This is the same idea only done in a different way.

"I shucked wolves only in the wintertime, and then only by the light of a full moon. I'll never forget the first time I tried it. It was one of those cold, clear

winter nights with a big yellow moon riding high in the sky—a time when wolf packs like to prowl.

"I put on my heavy-duty, long-handled, red underwear, woolen pants and a special long-sleeved buckskin shirt. Then I carefully smeared my right arm from wrist to shoulder with slippery bear grease. We always kept a supply of it on hand. Armed only with a big hunk of raw, red meat I went out alone into the frosty night.

"With my back close to the base of a steep cliff so nothing could get at me from behind, I stood still until I finally looked like a part of the winter scenery. The wolves coursing back and forth in the valley below in search of game soon smelled the raw meat and worked their way back upwind to locate it. Finally they reached the spot where I stood stock-still with the meat held high in my left hand.

"The pack moved up close to me in a small half circle. Then the leader leaped for the bait. Quick as a flash I jabbed my right fist and greased arm into his open mouth and straight down his throat. This made him gag and gasp for breath instead of biting me. As quick as a wink I reached right through the animal and grabbed it by the tail. Then I pulled my arm back swiftly and there was the wolf turned completely inside out. I snapped the whole thing sharply and the carcass came loose from the skin and fell to the ground. Dropping the fresh skin at my feet, I faced the rest of the animals and held the bait up high again."

"Why Grandpa, you undressed the wolf!"

"Yes, or shucked it. It was all done so fast that the other wolves didn't understand what had happened.

Then the second one took its turn with a flying leap at the meat. In the bat of an eye I shucked it, too. Soon I had the whole pack.

"When the night's fun was over and no more wolves showed up for the meat, I took the skins home, stretched them out to dry and salted them. Later I sold them to a fur buyer for a higher than regular price because they had no bullet holes in them or marks made by the jaws of a trap. I can't begin to tell you how many wolves I caught in this fashion. When word of this stunt got around, I became famous as the wolf-shucker of the Catskills."

It was Grandma's voice that brought me back to reality: "Frank, it's late and time for bed."

As I thanked them and said good-night, Grandpa's parting words were: "The next time you're playing with Mart in his father's barn take a good look at the wolfskin robe used by his great-grandfather. If there are no bullet holes in the hides, the chances are that I shucked 'em."

Popcorn

I SMELLED POPCORN AS I STEPPED THROUGH THE DOOR-
way that led to Grandma's pantry and kitchen. She was
standing at the stove shaking the long-handled popper
to the sharp sound of bursting kernels.

"They pop like firecrackers, Grandma."

"Yes, they do," Grandma said. "Sit right down at
the table. You're just in the nick of time."

"Hello, Frank. I hope you're hungry tonight. I'll
need a lot of help," announced Grandpa from his armchair.

The big tin pan on the back part of the stove was
soon heaped high with popped corn to which Grandma
added melted butter and salt. She brought it to the
table along with three wooden bowls.

Grandpa laid aside his paper, removed his metal-
rimmed spectacles and commented: "We can thank the
Indians for a lot of things like beans, squash, pumpkins
and maple sugar, but I think their best gift to the white
man was corn. And I can't think of anything better to
eat on a cold wintry night than fresh buttered popcorn."

When the bowls were emptied a second time,

Grandpa said: "I'll never forget an odd thing that happened to me years ago. We were having a stretch of
Indian summer, and the weather in the Catskills had
turned uncomfortably warm. I had stripped the ears of
corn from the stalks in the field and was hauling them
back to the barn in the lumber wagon, fitted out with
a high rack so I could carry a big load.

"On one of these trips the oxen were hauling our
whole year's crop of popcorn. As we were coming along
the lane with the sun beating down upon us and not
a breath of wind stirring, it got so infernally hot that
all of a sudden the entire load popped with a terrific
explosion. The corn burst up out of the rack with such
force that it threw me off the top of the load. Luckily,
I fell to one side and had time to scramble out of the
way or I'd have been smothered beneath the avalanche
of popcorn that buried the wagon out of sight. When
the oxen heard the noise, they stopped and turned their
heads around to see what had happened. Being near-
sighted, as all cattle are, they thought the great white
mound behind them was a huge snowbank, so they lay
right down in front of it and froze to death.

"The tremendous noise of the bursting popcorn was
the last sound I heard for several days. The shock of
the blast temporarily put my ears out of commission.
It's a terrible thing to suddenly be living in a world of
complete silence. But I gradually got over my deafness."

"What did you do with all that popcorn and the
frozen oxen?"

"I'm coming to that. I'd planned to sell this old yoke
of oxen before winter set in and use a younger pair

I'd raised and broken in. But now it was too late. I walked down the lane to the barn, yoked up the young pair to the stoneboat, went back, rolled the frozen carcasses over onto it and hauled them back to the barnyard. After they had thawed out, I butchered them, hauled the meat back to the big stack of popcorn and froze it again. Then I hung it up in the icehouse for our supply of fresh beef for the winter.

"Usually I stored our hay in the loft of the barn. That year I sold the whole crop to the neighbors, drew the great heap of popcorn home and piled it in the haymow. The horses and cattle ate it all that winter and thrived on it, although toward spring they did get a little jumpy."

"Did you eat any of the popcorn out of the haymow?"

"I'm glad you asked that. No! It was much too dirty and stale to be eaten by people. I'd been wondering what I was going to do for fresh popcorn during the winter so I finally went back to the field and gathered up all of the nubbins I could find."

"Nubbins?"

"They're small imperfect ears. Usually I just left them for the chipmunks and squirrels. I managed to collect several bushels, but they were mostly cobs with only a few kernels on them, although I did notice that the kernels were unusually large. I put them in burlap bags and hung them on pegs in the barn where they were safe from mice.

"One night around Thanksgiving time I got hungry for popcorn so I shelled a few nubbins, threw a handful of kernels in the corn popper and shook it over the bed of coals in the fireplace in the old homestead. The first couple of kernels that popped did so with such force that they blew the popper to pieces and the coals flew out into the room. I had to pick them up in a hurry with the fire tongs or they would have set the place on fire."

"Gee, Grandpa, you might have been hurt."

"I didn't dare pop any more of that corn crop for fear it might blow my head off. So I just left it in the barn and as the months went by forgot all about it.

"The following spring I decided to clear a patch of land and farm it. After I'd felled the trees and hauled away the logs the next step was to pull out the stumps. This was always mighty hard work. About this time I remembered the popcorn hanging in the barn. I went back and filled my pockets with it. Then I dug a small hole under one of the stumps, built a fire in it, threw in a half dozen big kernels . . . and ran. In a few seconds the corn popped and blew out the stump. I had a popcorn that was better and cheaper then blasting powder. In a short time I blew out all the stumps.

"I still had a couple of handfuls of that corn left and wondered what to do with it. It was just too dangerous to have around. Finally, just to get rid of it, I built a fire on the ground in a low spot in the pasture, put all of the kernels in an old wooden sap bucket and threw it on the fire. I must have run fifteen rods before the thing exploded. When the dirt and stones quit flying, I went back. Water was bubbling up in the bottom of the hole that had been blasted out. I had just made me a spring-fed watering pond for the livestock!"

The silence that followed was broken by Grandma's voice. "Frank, you had better run along to bed. And don't worry about all that popcorn you ate. It's this year's crop and won't hurt you."

King Apple

As soon as I was far enough along in school to be able to add small numbers, Grandpa taught me how to play dominoes. "The game will help you with your arithmetic," he said. "Besides, your grandmother likes to play, and we can make it a three-handed game."

Grandma thought it was a wonderful idea. She had been very patient, keeping quiet evenings while Grandpa entertained me with his stories. Here was some fun for her.

I thought it was great, too. An evening of dominoes allowed time between games for small talk about village doings. Time, too, for munching on good things to eat. And of course for Grandpa's jokes and riddles.

One particular evening Grandpa was the winner of three out of five games so Grandma said we should play a few more since it was still early. So we did and later she was smiling as I put the dominoes back in the box. She had won six out of ten games. I was still too young to be a challenger.

Now it was story time. Grandma turned to the paper. Grandpa lit his pipe.

"When I went after the cows this afternoon, Grandpa, I walked through the orchard and way up high in one of the trees I saw a great big red apple. It was the only one left on the whole tree and I tried to knock it down with a stone but I couldn't hit it. It was back near the stone wall."

"I know the tree you mean, Frank. It's a King. When we picked apples, we didn't see it among the leaves. Anyway it was up so high we couldn't reach it without a sky hook."

Grandma coughed and pointed to the bowl of apples in the middle of the table. "Help yourself," she said. "King apples are mighty good but they don't keep like these Northern Spies."

Grandpa moved closer. "Speaking of King apples reminds me of an experiment I tried many years ago when I was young and foolish."

"One warm sunny day in early September I was walking through the orchard and noticed that the apples on the King tree were bigger than usual. I picked the biggest one I could reach and looked at it. It was nearly as large as a baby's head. King apples were not only good eating, but they were noted for the amount of juice in them. A pint-size King apple contained a quart of juice. It was under such pressure that if you punched a hole in the skin of a ripe one the juice would squirt out like a tiny geyser."

"What's a geyser, Grandpa?"

"It's a hot spring that shoots out jets of water from time to time.

"The best cider was made from the juice of the King apple. As I looked at the big apple in my hand, I got

an idea for an experiment. I had been reading a story
about Luther Burbank who was famous all over the
world because he'd learned how to make new kinds of
fruits, vegetables and flowers by cross-breeding or com-
bining two different things. He crossed the plum and
the apricot to produce a new kind of fruit called the
plumcot. He learned how to grow cactus plants without
any spines. He improved or changed potatoes, toma-
toes, squashes, berries, even flowers by crossing different varieties.

"What, I wondered, could I do with this King apple
that had never been done before, to see if I could make
a new discovery?

"I climbed over the stone wall and walked through
the cornfield on the other side. Big fat pumpkins growing on green snake-like vines lay in the rows between
the cornstalks. All at once I knew what I would do.

"I put the apple on the ground beside the biggest
pumpkin I could find. From among the stubble beyond
the fence I picked up a dry, hollow rye straw. With it
I punched a hole through the vine near the pumpkin.
Then I pushed the other end into the King apple so
that the straw made a bridge or pipeline connecting
the two. The juice in the apple began flowing across
into the vine and on into the pumpkin. As the pressure
inside the apple went down, it began to shrink and
dry up until all of the juice was forced over into the
pumpkin. In a few days the apple withered away, the
rye straw fell out and the hole in the pumpkin vine
sealed over. My special pumpkin kept right on growing
as if nothing had happened.

"Would my experiment be a success? Would the pumpkin have an apple flavor? Only time would tell.

"As the days grew shorter and the nights grew cold and the corn was cut and shocked, the pumpkins too were harvested and piled in a heap in the barn. They were sorted over from time to time as smaller ones were selected for pies. The big special one because of its great size and rich golden color was held back for the Thanksgiving church social.

"A few days before Thanksgiving the enormous pumpkin was sawed into sections with a crosscut saw and several of the neighbor women carried pieces home to make the pies. When brought to the church supper everyone said they were the best smelling and best looking pumpkin pies seen in the village as far back as anyone could remember.

"The supper went along as planned but most everybody held back on the dinner so as to have room for a big piece of pumpkin pie. With the first bite it became the hit of the evening. There was a near stampede for a second, and even a third piece. The men wanted to know if the seeds had been saved. They all wanted some to plant in their gardens the next spring.

"Pretty soon the supper began to get out of hand. There was more loud talking and off-key singing; more bragging, more stories told, and more arguments started at that Thanksgiving social, yes, and more headaches the next day than ever before or since in the history of our mountain village. Why even the women were singing and slapping the men on their backs."

"What made everybody so happy, Grandpa?"

"The preacher came to call on me the next day when he got to feeling better and asked me what I did to that giant pumpkin to cause a near riot. I told him about my experiment, and this is what we figured out must have happened: The warm fall sunshine heated up the rye straw and the coiled pumpkin vine so that the juice from the apple started to ferment as it flowed across. It filled the pumpkin with hard cider; and when that pumpkin was baked into pies, they had the kick of a mule."

Grandpa cast a sly glance in the direction of Grandma. There was a twinkle in his eye. "This was the first, and last, time that I tried to be the Luther Burbank of the Catskills. Your grandmother made me promise that!"

Fog

"GUESS WHAT I BROUGHT YOU, GRANDMA."

Grandma placed her darning back in its shallow wicker basket and looked at the bulging cloth bag I had placed on the table in front of her.

"From what it says on the bag, it's five pounds of sugar, but from the bumps on the sides it looks like it's full of . . . let me see now . . . Marbles? . . . Prune pits? . . . Pebbles? . . . I give up! You'll have to tell me."

"Open it up and see."

Her strong fingers quickly loosened the string and out poured a pile of fat, brown nuts onto the table.

"Why, Frank. Where did you get them? These are the first chestnuts I've seen this fall."

"After school Clifford and I went down in the back pasture to where the three big chestnut trees grow behind the stone wall. The burrs are open after the frost we had a few nights ago, and there were lots of them on the ground."

"Your grandfather likes them too. He should be back from the store any minute now. While he tells you your evening story, I'll get out the heavy skillet and we'll have roasted chestnuts. Listen! I think I hear him now."

The latch rattled and the door opened and in came Grandpa with a smile on his face. He said 'hello' to me, hung up his coat and hat, and walked briskly to the table where he spied the mound of chestnuts.

"Hey, where did these come from?"

"Frank just brought them in. Aren't they big ones though?"

"I'll say they are. And here's another surprise for you, Liza." From behind his back Grandpa produced a small striped brown paper bag and handed it to her.

Grandma sniffed at the top before opening it. "Peppermints! Good. Thank you. Who'll have one with me?"

"I'll pass mine up for a smoke now and try some chestnuts later," replied Grandpa and proceeded to light up his pipe while I hastily told Grandma I'd join her in a peppermint.

"It's getting quite foggy out," Grandpa announced as he went to his armchair and sat down.

"What makes fog, Grandpa?"

"Fog is like a cloud that's touching the ground. The air is so full of little specks of water that you can see it like you can see your warm breath on a cold day. Sometimes in late fall when we have warm days and cold nights, the fog can get real thick in the valleys."

"I'd be afraid of getting lost in it if I had to go out after dark."

"You could get lost even in the daytime. I remember one afternoon while I was shingling the barn roof, a bank of fog drifted in. I kept on working a little longer, but it got so thick I had to quit. I hunted around until I found the ladder and started to climb down to the ground. Just then a puff of wind cleared the air for a second. I looked up and by golly, I had worked out beyond the edge of the roof and had shingled over several square yards of fog. I didn't have time to go back up so I just left it there. Later one of our turkeys tried to roost on it and knocked it down.

"I hurried down to the barn to get the chores done before it got worse; but by the time I was finished, the fog was so dense I couldn't push my way through it to get back to the house. I didn't want to spend the night in the barn so I took a shovel and cut out chunks of the solid fog and threw them out behind the barn to get them out of the way. I kept at it until I had dug a tunnel all the way up to the house. When I woke up the next morning, the weather had turned freezing cold and the tunnel was still there. I used it several days as a walk-through before it melted and blew away.

"It's too bad, Grandpa, it couldn't have stayed there all winter to keep out the wind and snow."

"That would have been a big help. Later in the week I looked out behind the barn and found a big pile of frozen chunks of fog still there that I had thrown out when I dug the tunnel."

"Why didn't they melt like the rest of the fog?"

"They were on the north side where the sun didn't strike them. I picked one up and was surprised to find how light it was. And just to see what would happen, I carried about fifty of the chunks over to the icehouse and buried them in the sawdust so they would keep.

Later when the weather had turned cold and the wild ducks were coming down from the north, I got an idea. I dug a block of frozen fog out of the icehouse, took it out to the marsh before daylight and tied it to the boat. By the time the sun came up it had melted and made a perfect blind. It was like being hidden in the middle of a little cloud. I must have shot more ducks that fall than anybody else in the village."

"That was a real handy trick."

"It certainly worked. And I think there might be other good uses for frozen fog. Suppose you were lost in a fog and the weather turned cold and froze it. With a hunting knife you could cut it into blocks and make a hut like the igloo the Eskimos make from blocks of snow."

Grandma's voice broke the spell of the story hour as she invited us to come out of the fog and sample the roasted chestnuts.

Hero Worship

"WE'VE MISSED YOU, FRANK," GRANDMA SAID AS I walked into her kitchen. "Your mother told me you had a cold and she was keeping you in until you got over it. Did she dose you up with sulphur and molasses like she planned?"

"Yes, she did, and I didn't like the taste of it, but I'm all right now and went back to school today."

Grandpa put down his paper. "I hope you'll get caught up soon with the work you missed so you won't have to wear the dunce cap and sit in the corner."

"Clifford brought my books home and told me every day what the lessons were so I didn't get behind."

"Were you called on to recite today to see if you'd kept up?"

"Yes, and the teacher laughed and laughed when I told the class how you connected the big King apple to the pumpkin with a straw, and the pumpkin pies at the church social had a kick in 'em and everybody got noisy and had such a good time."

Grandpa looked at me in surprise and cleared his throat, but before he could say anything, Grandma spoke: "What in the world made you tell that story?"

"We are studying about farming in New York State, and the geography said fruit growing was important. When my turn came I told Grandpa's story about the King apple."

"Abe," Grandma said reprovingly, "I wonder if you should fill an eight-year-old boy's head with all these whoppers you've been telling? Pretty soon he won't have any room in it for his school work. I hope Miss Smith doesn't go out and tell that story all over the neighborhood."

Grandpa looked down at me and winked. "It's a good way to develop his imagination, Liza. Where would we get our inventors, scientists and writers if we didn't encourage our children to use their imaginations? Besides, Frank should know something about the folklore of the Catskills. His ancestors have lived in these parts for over two hundred and fifty years."

"And I like stories, Grandma. Even Miss Smith sometimes reads them to us when we finish our lessons on time. One I remember was about a man named Rip Van Winkle. He lived over in Catskill, just up the Hudson River from here. He went hunting in the mountains one day and met some funny little men who were playing ninepins. He helped them set up the pins, and when he got thirsty they gave him a drink out of a keg. After a while he got so tired out he laid down and slept for twenty years."

Grandma wasn't one to give up easily. "Oh! I know all about him. He was too lazy to work. All he wanted to do was hunt and fish."

Grandpa reached for his clay pipe and tobacco jar.

Deliberately he filled the bowl, walked to the cook-stove, took a tightly twisted paper squill from the tin holder on the wall, pushed the sliding panel above the firebox to one side, touched the squill to the glowing coals and lit his pipe. Perhaps all this gave him time to think up an answer.

Seated again in his armchair, Grandpa spoke: "From what I've read, storytelling is as old as the hills. Ages ago before people had learned how to write things down, the only way knowledge could be passed along was by word of mouth. Many tribes had wise old men who taught the children their customs and beliefs by means of stories."

"Grandpa, do you mean their history?"

"Yes, something like that. But it wasn't like school. They probably sat around a fire at the end of the day and told the stories before going to sleep. Or in warm weather under a shady tree. Many of the stories were based on real happenings, perhaps adventures the hunters had had. As the years went by, some were told so many times by so many different people that they were gradually changed until they became folk tales and legends."

"Abe, I think you've been reading too much. You sound like a schoolmaster or a preacher. If there's any truth left in those yarns you've been telling Frank, I miss my guess."

"But Grandma, Grandpa's stories are just as good as the ones our teacher reads us out of books, only different. The other day Miss Smith told us that Abraham Lincoln was a great storyteller. He made lots of friends with his jokes and stories when he was running for President. He must have been a lot of fun. One time he and a man agreed to swap horses sight unseen. Then they went to get their horses. The other man brought a bony, old horse that was so weak and skinny it could hardly walk. They called it 'crow-bait'. Then Mr. Lincoln showed up carrying his horse on his shoulder. It was a wooden sawhorse!"

"That was a sly trick," Grandma remarked shortly.

Grandpa smiled and stood up. "Mr. Lincoln was a smart country boy. He was close to the people and always made them happy by telling them stories. Much of the country was being settled then. There weren't many books to be had and most people couldn't read anyhow. A good storyteller always made a hit."

He fingered his fancy gold watch chain and took his watch from his vest pocket. "I think I'll go down to the store and get some tobacco before Levi closes up. I don't want to run out."

I looked up at Grandpa—a powerful, angular man standing well over six feet in height, with a short, square-cut crop of chin-whiskers.

After Grandpa had gone out, Grandma folded her knitting neatly, placed it in her workbasket and turned toward me. "When I was a school girl we weren't taught much besides the three R's—reading, 'riting and 'rithmetic. Maybe schooling is different now and the old-fashioned ways of teaching are out of date. Anyway I hope Miss Smith won't tell your Grandfather's King apple story all over the neighborhood."

"I won't tell any more of Grandpa's stories to the

class if you don't want me to."

"No, I don't mean that, Frank. The other stories are all right. But, you see, your grandfather is an elder in the church and I don't want anybody to get a wrong notion. Now I know you'd like a bite to eat before you go to bed."

"I sure would. I'm hungry."

Minutes later I was enjoying a bowl of bread and milk.

"Gee, Grandma, I think Grandpa is as smart as anybody in the whole country. I'll bet he can tell stories as good as Abraham Lincoln ever could."

"I'm glad you think so, Frank. Your grandfather was a great admirer of Mr. Lincoln."

"I think Grandpa looks a lot like the pictures of Mr. Lincoln that Miss Smith showed us."

"Many people have said the same thing. As long as he's gone to the store, maybe this is a good time to tell you why.

"Your grandfather and Mr. Lincoln had a number of things in common. Both had the given name of Abraham. Your grandfather was born in 1835 in a log farmhouse several miles up in the hills from here. Like all country boys in the backwoods he had only a few years of schooling before he took on a man's work of clearing land, felling trees, laying up stone fences, farming and hauling loads of bluestone from the quarries. But he always liked to read. When he was twenty years old he stood well over six feet tall and was just about the strongest man around here.

"About that time he began to hear a lot of talk about

Abraham Lincoln. He was also a country boy, born in a log cabin, and probably didn't go to school more than three years in his whole life. He educated himself. He grew to be a tall, strong man who at one time or other had been a rail-splitter, country storekeeper and finally a self-taught lawyer. He was always popular as a story-teller. People who saw pictures of Mr. Lincoln said Abe Du Mond looked quite a bit like him."

Grandma hesitated a second: "Your grandfather was twenty-six years younger and more filled out than the pictures I saw of Mr. Lincoln, so I guess you might say he was better-looking.

"When Mr. Lincoln was running for President, a little girl saw his picture and wrote him a letter. His face was so hollow and thin she told him she thought he would look better if he grew a beard. He did and when your grandfather heard about it he decided to grow one too to keep up the resemblance. So you see your grandfather copied Mr. Lincoln's looks, and as the years went by everybody around here began to call him Uncle Abe. Of course he couldn't hope to become President, but he could live by the example set by Mr. Lincoln, and he could tell stories!"

"Gee, Grandma, no wonder everybody likes Grand-pa. He's a great man even though he didn't get to be President. Anyway, he is the singing master and an elder at church and justice of the peace."

"More than that, Frank, he's looked up to as a good and kind man who has always tried to do what's right."

"I guess I'm lucky to have you and Grandpa."

"And we're glad you like to come in and see us. You

help make us feel young again and give us cheerful things to think about.

"Well, I guess we've had enough talk for one night. You'd better run along now and get your rest. You don't want to fall asleep in school tomorrow."

Cherry Tree Buck

THERE WAS THE SOUND OF STOMPING FEET ON THE BACK stoop. Grandma looked up from her darning: "Frank, hop up, will you and let your Grandfather in. He must have his hands full."

As I opened the back door, in walked Grandpa with a pile of wood in his arms so high that he could hardly see over it. He dropped the load in the woodbox beside the stove.

"Thank you, Frank. That wood warmed me the day I cut it. And it will feel good to have it warm me again on a night like this."

After taking off his heavy wraps and boots, Grandpa put on his slippers, moved his armchair closer to the stove and lit his pipe. "Well, Frank, what did you do today after school?"

"On the way home Clifford and I walked through the apple orchard. We saw lots of deer tracks where they'd been eating apples left on the ground. Clifford said he wished he'd been there with his twenty-two rifle, and we could have had venison to take home."

Grandpa smiled. "That brother of yours will be a good hunter some day. But he's still pretty young to hunt deer. Let's see! How old is he?"

"He's three years older than Frank," Grandma broke in.

"Well, he'd better keep practicing on red squirrels for a while yet."

"Grandpa, do you know any stories about deer? Clifford told me to ask you."

"Why, yes I do. When I was a young man still living back on the farm, I had a very unusual thing happen to me one winter when our meat supply ran low and I went out to get a deer.

"It was a bitter cold day in February, but I decided to bundle up extra warm and go anyway. I took my muzzle-loading rifle, powder horn and bullet pouch and headed for the big cedar swamp back of the pasture where deer yarded up every winter. I could almost always count on getting one there.

"I sat down on a stump beside a runway to wait. For a long time there were no signs of life. Then suddenly out of nowhere a big buck appeared carrying an unbelievably huge rack of antlers. I took aim and fired and the buck dropped to the ground. The bullet must have gone right through its body because it knocked a piece of bark off a hickory sapling on the other side of the runway.

"I ran forward, but before I could get to it the deer jumped to its feet, looked in my direction, and bounded out of sight. In that one second, though, I had a clear view of the animal and had the shock of my life. I had shot the famous cherry-tree buck of the Catskills—an animal held almost sacred by the people who lived

around there. What I had thought was an oversize spread of antlers had been the branches of a little tree growing on the buck's head. Had I stopped to think before shooting, I would have remembered that male deer had shed their antlers by that late in the winter.

"I knew if anyone ever found out that I had shot the cherry-tree buck, I'd be run out of the country. Luckily for me, it was so cold that morning that when the blood started to flow from the bullet holes, it froze solid on contact with the outside air and sealed the openings. This stopped the bleeding immediately. Before the weather warmed up about ten days later, the buck's wounds had healed completely. The bullet hadn't hurt it at all, and it lived to a ripe old age."

"Gee whiz, Grandpa! I'm glad you didn't hurt that deer. Was that a real live tree on its head?"

"Yes, Frank, it was a real tree—a cherry tree."

"But how could a tree grow out of the head of a deer?"

"It seems that some years before a small boy wanted to shoot off a gun so badly that he borrowed his father's, probably without permission. He managed to find enough powder to load it but couldn't locate any lead for bullets. As I understand it, his mother was pitting cherries at the time for some pies she was about to bake. The boy took a handful of cherry pits and put them in his pocket. Then he went out into the woods, loaded the gun with cherry pit bullets, and hid in the bushes. After a while he saw a little spotted fawn coming his way. When it came close enough, he took aim and fired. All of the cherry pits except one bounced harmlessly off the hide of the scared little deer and it ran away. This one cherry pit struck the little fawn high up on the forehead midway between the eyes and stuck there under the skin. After a while the cherry pit sprouted and produced a tiny seedling. As the deer grew larger it developed antlers and finally became a beautiful buck. The little cherry seedling became a small tree. The buck's antlers were normal in every way and were shed each midwinter but the tree remained in place although the leaves turned brown and were dropped every fall. Soon people living around there noticed this unusual deer with the shrubby tree on its head and it became known as the cherry-tree buck. Nobody ever would have dreamed of harming it.

"Every spring people would go out in the woods in the hope of seeing the buck with the cherry tree in full bloom. Imagine it! Bees buzzing around the flowers, birds sitting on the branches singing away. And all on the head of a deer. And then as the days passed the cherries ripened and the birds came back to eat the fruit. Only the birds ever figured out how to pick the cherries from that tree."

"I wish I could have seen the cherry-tree buck, Grandpa."

"I'm afraid, Frank, that was long before your time."

Minutes later, following a glass of milk and an oatmeal cookie, I was on my way to bed.

Just imagine! Robins eating cherries from a tree growing out of a buck deer's head!

Encounter With
a Panther

"How would you like to wipe the dishes for me, Frank, while you're waiting for your grandfather to finish his paper?"

"Sure, Grandma. From all the pans, I guess you baked bread today."

"Yes, I did. A little later I'll give you a slice with some cherry jam on it. After your grandfather's story the other night about the cherry-tree buck, I thought you might like some. These cherries came from the tree at the edge of the garden."

When the dishes were done and put away in the cupboard, Grandpa looked up and cleared his throat: "I think Frank has earned his bread and jam tonight, Liza, and maybe an extra piece for not breaking any of your dishes."

This was the moment I'd been waiting for. "Ever since you told me about the cherry-tree buck, Grandpa, I've wanted to ask if you shot any more deer that day."

"No, Frank, I didn't. Because of my carelessness I got into a jam—and it wasn't cherry jam either—and was lucky to get out of it alive."

"How was that?"

"I was still upset about shooting the cherry-tree buck, but I went on farther into the swamp. There were many other deer in the yard, so it was just a question of time before I'd see another. Pretty soon I came to a spot where a big old pine tree had blown down. It was much too thick to climb over so I walked around the end where the broken roots rose high above my head. As I came to the other side, I saw something a few feet in front of me that almost scared me out of my wits. I stopped dead in my tracks. Crouching flat on its belly on the snow, ready to spring at me was a big panther. It must have measured all of nine feet in length from its nose to the tip of its tail. It bared its teeth and twitched its long tail like all cats do when they're excited.

"At this point it suddenly dawned on me that I'd forgotten to reload my gun. In the excitement of shooting the cherry-tree buck, I had made a foolish blunder that no hunter in wild country should ever be guilty of.

"I knew at once that I was in a tight spot and to get out of it alive I'd have to outwit a very dangerous animal. I was enough of a woodsman to know that the only way I could keep the big cat from springing on me and killing me with one blow of its powerful paw was to be very slow in every move I made so as not to excite it further. I also knew that man has some strange power over beasts; that most of them feel he is their master. If I could stand perfectly still and look steadily into its eyes, I might have a chance to think up some way to get the best of it. I might save my life.

"In time of danger a man's mind works fast. I thought almost at once of many things I might do, but

came back each time to my first thought—I must somehow reload my gun, doing it so slowly that I did not
alarm the panther.

"In slow motion I placed the butt end of the muzzle-
loader on the toe of my left boot. Holding it with my
left hand, I reached for the powder horn hanging on
the thong under my right arm. I lifted it ever so slowly
to my mouth and pulled out the wooden stopper with
my teeth. Gradually moving it over to the muzzle of
the gun I poured an extra large charge of powder down
into the barrel. Quietly placing the powder horn back,
I reached across my body for the bullet pouch, which I
had hung from its thong under my left arm, staring all
the time steadily into the eyes of the big cat. But try as
I might, I couldn't find it. It was gone! Apparently the

thong had come unhooked, and I had lost my precious bullets somewhere behind me.

"There I stood at the mercy of the panther with only a charge of powder in the gun and no bullets. I became paralyzed with fear, not knowing what to do next. The panther all of this time continued to crouch in the snow, still trying to decide if this quiet two-legged thing in front of it was an enemy.

"How long I stood there, I don't know. It seemed like ages. Then suddenly I began to see spots in front of my eyes. They were falling, shiny objects. As I looked through them into the eyes of the panther, I realized that I had broken out into a cold sweat. The beads of perspiration that were coming out on my forehead were freezing and dropping off to the ground in front of me.

"I had a sudden wonderful thought. I cupped my hand and caught a handful of these little round balls of ice and dropped them down into the barrel of the gun. Then I managed to get a percussion cap from my pocket and into place under the trigger. I was just about to move the gun into firing position when the panther, at last sensing that something was wrong, flexed its muscles and sprang at me.

"I swung the gun in the direction of the oncoming beast and fired from the hip. There was a loud explosion and out of the gun came, not bullets, but a thin stream of water. The beads of sweat had been melted by the heat of the powder. But the air was so cold that the little squirt of melted sweat froze instantly into a sharp, thin icicle that hit the panther right between the eyes and punctured its skull. It hit the ground, rolled over, twitched its hind legs and died."

"Golly, that was a close call. Did you ever find your bullet pouch?"

"Yes, I did, hanging on the end of a broken root of the pine tree. Losing it was the best thing that ever happened to me. If I had shot that panther with a lead bullet, it wouldn't have hurt it any more than the bullet hurt the cherry-tree buck. A real bullet would have caused bleeding, the wound would have instantly sealed shut as the blood came in contact with the cold air, and the panther would have killed me. The beads from the sweat of my brow had done what no bullet could ever have done because, you see, the body heat of the animal melted the icicle and the panther died of water on the brain."

Sour Soil
& Hollow Trees

GRANDMA LOOKED UP FROM THE BOWL OF CRACKED black walnuts she was sorting.

"Your grandfather just went out to the woodshed, Frank, to pile up the hard maple and oak he worked up today for our winter supply."

"I'll go help him, Grandma. Maybe we can get through so he'll have time to tell me a story."

The pleasant smell of sawdust and freshly cut wood filled the shed. Grandpa was putting some sticks on the top of a long row. He was so tall he was sliding them into place just under the rafters.

"I came out to help you," I announced.

He turned around. "That's fine, Frank. You're just in time to start a new tier for me. You're built closer to the ground and can stoop over a lot easier than I can. I've been sawing and splitting most of the day and this will give me a chance to set here a spell and rest my back. Then when you get up a ways I'll pitch in and we'll work together."

Twilight was settling in the valley when we finished our work and went back into the house.

"We make a good team, Liza," Grandpa declared as

we entered the kitchen. "Frank'll be big enough to work on the woodpile one of these days, and I'll make him a saw buck of his own. Every fall some of the neighbors are looking for a strong boy to buck up and split their firewood for winter. It'll be a good way for him to earn some money."

Grandma was stirring something on the stove. "That's a good idea, Abe. It beats all how much wood a kitchen stove eats up in cold weather. By the way, I'll have a treat for you two a little later. Something for your sweet tooth after your storytelling is over."

After we had washed our hands in the tin basin, Grandpa lit his pipe and made himself comfortable in his armchair. "Cutting stovewood today reminded me of the time I discovered that crab apples could be so sour they would eat the heart out of black walnut trees.

"It all happened back on the old farm where we had a grove of walnuts growing on a piece of rich bottomland. I wanted to use the land for a patch of corn, so I thought I'd kill two birds with one stone as the saying goes: cut off the trees and sell the walnut logs at a good price, and on the cleared land grow the extra corn I needed for the cattle and hogs.

"First I had to clean out a bunch of scrubby wild crab apples that had sprung up in the open spaces where they got the sunlight they needed. Then I started on the walnut trees. The saw bit into the first one like I was cutting butter with a warm knife, and I had it down in a jiffy. I was surprised to find it was as hollow as an empty barrel. The heartwood had disappeared and all that was left was an empty shell. Even the branches were hollow. I tackled the next one and that was hollow, too. And so was every single one of them—not a sound stick of walnut in the lot. They were worthless for lumber but at least they'd do for firewood, so I hauled them off to one side out of the way.

"Then I pulled out the stumps and planted my corn. The days went by and nothing came up. I waited and waited. Finally I dug into the rows and discovered that every kernel had disappeared. I planted the land a second time and again nothing came up. There was no sign that the soil had been disturbed, so I knew that crows or squirrels hadn't dug up the seed."

"That was funny, Grandpa."

"It certainly was. I didn't know which way to turn. The whole plan was a failure, all my hard work was for nothing, and nobody could tell me what was wrong. Then one day I got to talking about it with the schoolmaster. He said maybe the professor who taught chemistry at the Academy in Kingston might test a sample of the soil for me, and so I put some in a bag and took it with me the next time I went to town. The professor tried some chemicals on it and said the seed corn was being eaten by a strong acid that was in the ground. When I told him about the hollow walnut trees, he said this was further proof. The roots had carried the acid up into the trees, and the sap had become so strong it had eaten away the heartwood.

"Then I remembered the crab apple trees. 'There's your trouble' he explained. 'The apples that fell off those trees were so sour and crabby they ruined the soil. You probably never will be able to grow anything on the land, unless you sweeten it up'."

"Did you do it?"

"Not for several years. Then I got an idea. I planted some cucumber seeds and poured hot strained honey around them. They sprouted and I raised the biggest crop of cucumber pickles ever grown in the Catskills."

"That was great, Grandpa. You had something to show for all your work after all. Did the hollow walnut trees make good firewood?"

"I never got around to cutting them up, and I am glad I didn't. Next year a lumber buyer from a barrel factory in Kingston came around. When he saw the big pile of seasoned hollow trees he bought the whole kit and caboodle—from the logs right down to the branches. Later I was told the factory turned out a brand new line of walnut goods that ranged from napkin rings and toothpick holders to pails, casks and barrels of every size under the sun.

"So you see after all my trouble and worry, that cloud turned out to have a silver lining."

After Grandpa's sour soil story, Grandma's black walnut fudge never tasted sweeter!

Quick Freeze

WHEN I STEPPED THROUGH THE PANTRY DOORWAY INTO her warm friendly kitchen, Grandma was busy cutting a big pile of calico and muslin into smaller pieces.

Grandpa put down his paper and lit his pipe: "We're in for a cold snap. The geese were flying south this afternoon and Overlook Mountain stands out so clear it seems like it's been moved up a mile closer to us."

Grandma nodded: "It's high time I was getting these squares cut out so we can have a quilting bee. We'll need another bed cover this winter. And maybe I'd better get our heavy underwear out of moth balls pretty soon."

"Grandpa, how can geese tell when cold weather is coming?"

"I don't rightly know, Frank. Perhaps they can sense things that we can't. They don't often make mistakes in predicting the weather, but when they do they can be in real trouble. I remember one time years ago—"

"Abe, excuse me for butting in. Before you start Frank's story I wish you'd trim this lamp wick. It's burning high on one side and starting to smoke."

The job done, Grandpa returned to his armchair

and continued: "It was late afternoon in November, and I had just finished milking the cows. As I looked through the open barn door at the fresh fall of snow on top of Overlook Mountain, I heard voices overhead. I stepped outside and looked up. Several flocks of geese were flying in V-shaped formation toward the South. I knew then a cold spell was coming.

"The spring-fed pond at the foot of the hill behind the barn had not frozen over yet. I was thankful for this because the cattle could still drink out of it and this saved me the work of pumping water from the well for them every day.

"While I was bedding down the horses and cows with straw, I could hear more geese coming over. Then all was quiet outside. I had finished throwing a little more hay in the mangers and was about to set the two pails of milk outside and close the barn door when I heard the honking of still another flock. It was almost dark now. Their calls grew louder and louder until it sounded as if they were almost in the barn. They circled overhead a couple of times, then they settled down on the pond below the hill. It was a small patch of water for such a big flock, but they could huddle together and be safe for the night. The fish, frogs and small turtles in the water under them certainly wouldn't hurt them.

"I quietly closed the barn door and carried the milk up to the cabin. I was young then and single, living with my folks up in the mountains several miles from here. After supper I went out and helped my father carry in some short logs to keep the fireplace fire going all night. It was getting very cold. The stars glittered in a clear sky. My mother put heavy quilts on the beds. During the night the timbers made loud noises from the cold.

"When daylight came I got up and looked out-of-doors. A heavy frost had covered everything with white. Then I remembered the geese that had come down to spend the night on the little pond. A wild goose dinner would be a welcome treat. And my mother had said she needed some goose down for some pillows she wanted to make. So I loaded the shotgun and went outside. The geese were honking as if they were all excited. I lined up behind a straw stack so they couldn't see me and sneaked up within gun shot. Peeking out toward the pond I was surprised to see that it had frozen over during the night and every last goose was caught fast by its feet in the ice.

"There was now no need to waste powder and lead on a band of birds that were stuck fast, so I leaned my gun against the stack and ran down the hill. When the geese saw me coming, they set up a louder racket and beat their powerful wings and tried to get away. But the ice held their feet, and they got nowhere. As I came closer, they were so scared they flapped harder and all flew up into the air together taking the frozen pond with them, leaving an empty hole in the ground where the pond had been.

"I ran back for my gun, and as the flock passed overhead on its way south I fired a blast at them. All I got for my trouble were some large chunks of ice that fell out of the sky and nearly brained me. The layer of ice clinging to their feet made a good shield between them and the shot. Honking wildly, they were soon gone.

"According to stories we heard and read in the paper later, people for miles around were astonished to see a flock of noisy geese flying southward carrying a small iceberg attached to their feet."

"Didn't they get tired out pretty soon, carrying all that weight?"

"They got tired, all right. But the farther south they went the warmer the weather became so the ice gradually melted and the load got lighter. People in cities along the way were flabbergasted when out of a clear sky they were showered with fish, frogs and polliwogs that kept falling from the melting ice. And the lady in Baltimore who found a mud turtle frozen in the center of a chunk of ice floating in her fish pond never knew it had been flown in from the Catskill Mountains by special goose delivery."

"I hope the geese got to wherever they were planning to spend the winter, Grandpa, without any more trouble. Did the pond ever fill up again with water?"

"Oh, yes! Good springs never quit running, even in winter."

Grandma pushed aside her quilting squares and stood up. "It's time you were off to bed, Frank. Morning comes early, and you mustn't be late for school."

My evening was complete—almost! "I'm hungry, Grandma. May I have a cookie?"

"I'm afraid I don't have any tonight. I've been too busy to bake the past few days. I'll get you a glass of milk, and before you go I'll give you a couple of lemon drops. They'll last until you're undressed and in bed."

Cold Weather

GRANDPA AND GRANDMA WERE SITTING NEAR THE STOVE as I walked into the kitchen. The woodbox against the wall was piled high with seasoned hardwood. On the back of the stove a teakettle purred contentedly.

"Come and sit over here by the fire, Frank," invited Grandma. "It's a real cold night."

As I moved a chair between my grandparents, Grandpa lowered his pipe and spoke: "The sky is clear and the wind is out of the north. It's going to be a cold one, all right. I bedded the stock down extra heavy tonight and let the chickens sleep in the barn."

"Listen to the wind rattle the shutters on the side of the house," said Grandma as she moved a little closer to the stove.

"How cold do you think it's going to be, Grandpa?"

The shutters rattled again, and even in my long winter underwear I trembled at the sound. It was comforting to have big people around on such a wild night.

"I wouldn't be surprised if it went down a long ways below zero on the kind of thermometer we use today."

"What do you mean? Were thermometers ever different?"

"Yes, they were. Years ago when I was a young man we measured the temperature in feet and inches. It got much colder way back then. We had a thermometer as tall as a man. It hung from a branch of the apple tree alongside the house. One morning I looked out and the mercury, or quicksilver as we used to call it, had gone down so far that it had knocked the bottom out of the glass tube. I went outside and hunted around in the snow, but I couldn't find it."

"Where did it go?"

"It must have gone down several feet below zero in the night. Even then it was still so cold that the steam from my breath froze solid in front of me and fell on the snow at my feet. I picked up a chunk, and it looked like frozen sea foam.

"Another thing I noticed was that everything was so quiet. When one of my neighbors went past, I asked him if he knew how cold it was, and I couldn't even hear my own voice. He looked at me, and I saw his lips move but I didn't hear him say anything either. The blacksmith rode past in his sleigh, but the sleigh-bells didn't chime. More people came by and we got together out in the road but nobody could hear a word anybody said. We wondered if the bitter cold had made us deaf. About that time the sun came out from behind a cloud. We had quit trying to talk to each other, yet all at once we could hear voices. We couldn't understand a thing that was being said because it sounded just like a lot of words that didn't make sense. A few seconds later the sun went under the clouds again, and the talking stopped. This happened several times."

"What do you think it was?"

"When the cold spell was over, and we could talk, we figured that the sounds of our voices had frozen solid. When the sun came out and shone down through the branches of the trees, it hit the frozen conversation in spots and thawed out words here and there. No wonder we couldn't make any sense to what was being said."

"That must have been scary. Did it ever happen again?"

"Yes, it did. Another time I was out camping for a week with Jim Snyder, a neighbor. We were deer hunting. A cold spell came on and it got so bad our conversation froze up completely. One night I was frying some venison over the campfire and started talking to myself. Then a funny thing happened. The frozen words fell into the frying pan and thawed out. For a minute it sounded like the frying pan was talking."

Grandma stood up. "Abe, you ought to tell your cold weather tales in the summertime. They'd cool things off when it's hot outside. I think I'll make some hot cocoa to warm us up."

"There's a good bed of coals in the stove, Liza. Maybe we could have some toast to go with it. What do you say, Frank?"

"Oh, I can always eat. How long did the cold spell last, Grandpa, that busted your big thermometer?"

"I don't remember exactly. But it was several days and it gave me all kinds of trouble."

"How was that?"

"The days got dark so early at that time of the year that I had to do my barn chores by kerosene lantern.

The very next night after the mercury smashed the bottom out of the thermometer, it was so cold when I walked back to the house that the flame on the lantern froze solid and I couldn't blow it out."

"What in the world did you do?"

"I carried it into the house and set it near the fireplace to thaw out first. The next night the same thing happened. It was too much bother to wait around again for the flame to thaw out so I just broke it off with my fingers and threw it into the fire where it melted and finished burning."

"Didn't the milk freeze on your way up to the house?"

"Worse than that. When I milked the cows, it froze before it hit the pail. I ended up carrying it in my arms like a load of icicles. If the cold weather had lasted much longer, I probably would have been selling milk by the cord instead by the quart."

Grandma turned to me. "Your grandfather forgot to tell you about his wonderful discovery the next spring. According to what his mother told me after we were married, he was out plowing the kitchen garden in April. As he turned the oxen around near the house, he looked down into the bottom of the furrow and saw that he had uncovered a vein of silver metal. He rushed into the house all excited to tell his mother—that would be your great-grandmother—that he had found a quicksilver mine in the garden and they would be rich. She ran out and there was the missing column of mercury that had knocked the bottom out of the thermometer."

Grandpa smiled and reached for a slice of toast.

Hard Times

GRANDPA WAS PUTTING ON HIS HEAVY WRAPS AS I CAME into the kitchen one cold winter night.

"How would you like to take a trip with me out to the root cellar, Frank? Your grandmother needs some things, and you're just in time to help me."

"Sure, Grandpa, I'd like to."

"Then I'll wait for you while you run back and get on a heavy coat and your cap. The wind is right off the mountain tonight and has teeth in it. You'd better put on your felt boots, too, because the snow is drifting."

A trip to the root cellar was an event to look forward to. The entrance to it was outside the house, and was like going into a cold, spooky cave. It ran into the hill-side and the floor and side walls were mostly of rock.

I hurried back to the other side of the house and soon returned ready. Grandpa lighted the kerosene lantern, and we went out into the night. At the cellar door he lifted the latch, and we stepped in. The lantern cast soft shadows, and the moist, dark stones glistened as we moved along past bins and barrels containing potatoes, turnips, carrots, beets and apples, and crocks filled with mince meat, sauerkraut and other eatables.

Cured hams and slabs of bacon and dried beef hung from overhead beams. The air was heavy with a blend of many odors.

I held the lantern while Grandpa put a couple of pecks of apples in a burlap bag. "Your grandmother is going to bake some pies for the church social, and these Northern Spies will be just the thing. We'll have one to eat later."

A mixture of vegetables went into another sack.

"You and Grandma certainly have plenty to last you all winter," I said.

"Yes, it's been a good year. I can remember a time, though, back on the farm when we went without and had to tighten our belts before spring. I'll tell you about it when we get back to the house where we'll be more comfortable."

After we had taken off our wraps and were settled near the kitchen stove, Grandpa continued: "We had a very dry summer one year and the crops didn't amount to much. Then winter came on early, and the snow and cold held on until late spring. We got short on food both for ourselves and for the farm animals. Wild things had a tough time too, and a lot of them were driven by hunger to prowl around farm buildings trying to kill pigs, chickens, sheep, and even cattle if they could get to them. But it wasn't just the wolves and panthers we had to watch out for. Some of the small animals, like the bloodthirsty little weasels that could crawl through knot holes and cracks, were harder to keep out than the big ones.

"We had a good tight barn, so the cattle and pigs

were safe, but we lost so many chickens we finally put the last few in the woodshed alongside the house where we could watch them. Grain became so scarce and they got so thin that they dropped through the cracks between the boards and began to scratch around under the floor. If it hadn't been for the things they found to eat on the ground under the woodshed, I think they would have starved to death."

"I'll bet you didn't get many eggs that winter."

"No, we didn't, and the few the hens did lay were thin and flat and about the size of a silver dollar.

"We did manage to pull some through until spring, although it was a tight squeak. Funny thing about the chickens: Even when we let them outdoors and there was plenty of food for them to scratch for, they never did fatten up again. And they never did lay anything but thin, round eggs like little cartwheels.

"Later on, one of these skinny hens wanted to set so I let her keep her own clutch of eggs. When the chicks hatched, they were so thin they looked like pasteboard cutouts. She raised them all, and every one turned out to be a full-size rooster, but as thin as a board."

"They must have been hard to keep track of Grandpa, unless you looked at them sideways."

"That's right. They could walk right through a wide crack in the barn siding, but the worst part was they had no meat on their bones so I never did bother to cut off their heads."

"What happened to them?"

"One day a peddler came through with his wagon

and when he saw them he bought the whole bunch. Paid me a good price for 'em too."

"I wonder what he did with them?"

"Later I found out he sold them at a fancy price as combination weather vanes and alarm clocks. I guess they were the first and last living weather vanes that not only showed the direction of the wind but were guaranteed to crow about it at sunrise."

As the story ended, Grandma who had been busy at the kitchen work table, spoke up: "I'll have a treat ready for you soon. I've just cored three of these nice Spies and filled the centers with maple sugar. It's early yet, so while they finish baking I'd like to beat you two at a game of dominoes."

Barn Owls

GRANDMA TURNED FROM THE STOVE AND SMILED AS I walked into her kitchen one evening in early April. "Your grandfather's gone down to the store with three dozen eggs the hens laid today. They're laying good at last, more than we need, so I'm selling them while they're fresh. My egg money will come in handy for extras on the trip I plan to take down to Brooklyn next month to see your Aunt Elizabeth."

The door opened and Grandpa entered with a bag of stick candy and some change, which he handed to Grandma. "The treat's on me, and the hens have added forty-five cents to your teapot savings bank."

Grandma curtsied. "Thank you, Mister D. I'm grateful to all concerned. But what I can't figure out is this —why don't hens lay lots of eggs during the winter when the price is up instead of in the spring when the price is down?"

Grandpa was still smiling as he hung up his hat and walked to his armchair: "Spring is here and that makes the difference. With more sunlight and warm weather, I guess we're all happier. And from the way the hens are cackling and laying, I know they feel better, too."

"Grandpa, if Grandma wants more egg money before she goes to visit Aunt Elizabeth wouldn't it be great if you could teach the hens to lay more than one egg a day?"

"Frank, you remind me of something that happened to your grandmother and me soon after we were married."

"Now Abe, don't let your spring fever get the best of you. And Frank, you'd better have a stick of sassafras candy to go along with your story."

Grandpa laughed and motioned for me to sit on the footstool in front of him.

"Late one afternoon I climbed up the ladder to the loft to pitch some hay down to the horses. It was April, and at that time of the year the loft was almost empty. As I walked to the far end, two big spooky things almost scared me out of my wits; they rose suddenly from almost under my feet and then vanished. I guess I must have jumped about six feet in the air.

"I knew lots of things made themselves at home in barns: swallows, pigeons, raccoons, skunks, even tramps. But I had never seen ghosts before.

"I looked around and made out two light-colored figures as big as babies peering at me from the beam over my head. I yelled and waved my arms and they flew out the open window at the end of the loft. They were barn owls."

"I'll bet you wanted to get them out of there for good, Grandpa."

"No. Barn owls are good to have around because they catch rats and mice. They're better mousers than cats.

And they don't eat chickens as most people think.

"Since they were a pair and this was their nesting season, I looked around me on the floor and found five large white eggs in a corner on a few wisps of hay. Out of curiosity I kept an eye on the nest, and about three weeks later the eggs produced five odd-looking, fuzzy baby owls. Every few days I climbed up to see how they were getting along, and finally when they were almost big enough to fly, I came up with what seemed to me to be a very clever idea. I caught two of them and put them in the chicken yard, which was enclosed with wire. They wouldn't hurt the chickens and it would cost me nothing to feed them because they could catch the rats and mice that came at night to steal the uneaten grain.

"As I had expected, this plan worked out very successfully. But as time passed an unusual thing happened. The owls and the chickens got to being on such friendly terms that they paired off and set up housekeeping together. When the eggs hatched as a result of this mating, the chicks were a strange combination of the looks of both. By now I was so interested in what had happened that I let these hybrids grow up as freaks to show the neighbors.

"Then there came the day when they began to lay and now I found that I had really struck it rich because they had the hen's habit of laying an egg during the daytime and the owl's urge to lay an egg during the night. As a result, I got two eggs a day from these mixed-up birds . . . one on the day shift, so to speak, and one on the night shift. This increase in egg production at no extra cost was a mighty welcome addition to our food supply.

"Well, when this thing had been going on for some time I got to thinking it over and one day said to your grandmother—'You know, I've got an idea. As long as we have these hybrid fowls doing double duty and laying eggs at a two-for-one rate, I think we might as well sell the hens to the butcher. Then we won't have to raise corn to feed them and we can use the land for growing something else.' And your grandmother agreed.

"As I turned around, there stood our old rooster right outside the door listening. He must have heard every word I said. He let out a loud squawk and high-tailed it back to the barn as fast as he could run. Then he started clucking for all he was worth, and the hens came a-running to see what wonderful morsel he had found for them. And when all of the hens had gathered around, can't you imagine what he told them: 'Girls, I've got news for you! You're all going to lose your heads unless you get busy' . . . and he told them what he had just heard.

"And do you know, he had those hens so scared they went right to the nests and each of them laid an egg that was bigger than usual. Believe it or not, they were so afraid of having their heads chopped off, they kept on laying eggs that were slightly larger every day until finally they were so big it took only six of them to make a dozen."

"But Grandpa! I ——"

"Just a minute, Frank. When I've finished my story you'll have a chance to ask questions.

"Now the whole situation had changed. With the hens laying these whopper eggs at the rate of six to a dozen, it looked like they were winning out in their egg-laying contest with the owl hybrids. The hybrid owls, on the other hand, probably didn't give a hoot because they were sure they were easily the winners.

"Well, anyway, this went on for quite a while until one Sunday at dinner I turned to your grandmother while we were eating one of these mixed-up fowls and said: 'Did you ever stop to think that in eating these hybrids we're eating part owl? And a part of each of the eggs they lay must be owl egg?'

"And your grandmother replied: 'I have often thought of that, and I spleen against them when I think that part of every mouthful I eat of that meat is barn owl that lives on rats and mice.'

"So I went out and got rid of all the hybrid birds. In a few days I found that I had made a great mistake. Just as soon as the hens saw that the hybrid owls were gone and they were no longer in danger of getting the ax, they stopped laying the jumbo-size eggs. They knew the competition was over and they didn't have to make that special effort to lay the big eggs. So their eggs began to get smaller and smaller from day to day until at last they were right back to the regular size.

"And so was lost to science and the world this marvelous cross between owl and fowl.

"Now Frank, what did you want to say a while back?"

"In school, Grandpa, we learned it always takes twelve things to make a dozen."

"It's late, Frank, so off you go to bed," Grandma said softly. "And don't count eggs in your sleep. Only in your grandfather's story could six ever equal a dozen."

Sweat Fish

As I WALKED THROUGH THE PANTRY DOORWAY INTO Grandma's kitchen she greeted me with a surprised: "Why Frank, where did you get the pretty white flowers? Are they for me?"

"Yes, Mama said I should bring some to you. I got them from a little tree on the hillside behind the church."

"Thank you. They're a sure sign of spring. I'd better put them in water right away."

Grandpa looked up from his paper: "Shadbush! When they're in bloom the shad are running up the Hudson River from the ocean. The fishermen must be putting out their nets."

"What do they come up the river for, Grandpa? That's a long ways."

"They do it every spring to lay their eggs in fresh water. When they hatch, the little fish stay in the river until fall. Then they swim downstream to live in the salt water of the ocean until they're old enough to come back and lay their eggs."

"I never knew that fish traveled around like that."

"Oh yes. Salmon do the same thing. But did you ever

hear of fish traveling hundreds of miles without ever getting into the water?"

"No I didn't. How in the world could they do that?"

While Grandpa filled and lighted his pipe, Grandma hummed as she cut and arranged the sprays of shadbush in a pitcher.

Then Grandpa began: "This story is as old as time. It started way back in the beginning of everything. The Good Lord had worked hard for six days creating the world and everything in it and was getting ready to quit and go home to rest up on the Sabbath. He looked up at the sun and saw that he still had a little time to do one more thing so he created the sweat fish.

"Now the sweat fish was not like any other fish on earth. It was meant to live where the weather was always cold. For this reason it was placed up near the North Pole so there would always be plenty of snow and ice to keep it cool. For food it ate snow fleas and ice worms.

"Sweat fish had extra large sweat glands. When they wanted to go for a swim or take a bath, a group or school of them would come out in the open where the sun could warm them up. Their sweat glands would start to work, and pretty soon they had a pond of their own sweat to swim in.

"As the years passed, a strange thing happened. The weather became colder and colder over a period of many years. The ice and snow kept piling up until it finally became so high that great glaciers spread over what is now Canada and the northeastern part of the United States. When the glaciers moved southward, the sweat fish living on them came, too. One of these slow moving ice fields pushed down into the Catskills. On its surface was a big school of sweat fish. Living in the deep cracks in the ice they didn't realize they were in for trouble. Then one sunny day the ice that connected them with the main part of the glacier to the north melted away and they were left stranded. The weather was now turning warmer again and it was too late for them to get back on the ice that was slowly pulling back toward the North Pole. The mass of ice they were on gradually melted entirely away and the sweat fish were finally left high and dry on the top of a mountain. For the first time they were really warm and uncomfortable and very unhappy. They flopped about on the ground and gradually slid down the steep slope into the valley below. Crowded together in the heat, the sweat began to pour out of their glands and pretty soon they had made their own pond to swim in. They had no way of ever getting back up north to the land where it was always cold, so the Catskill Mountains became their home."

"Do we still have sweat fish around here?"

"I haven't seen any in recent years but they were here when I was a young man. I used to go fishing for them once in a while. It was a lot of fun. They couldn't be caught like ordinary fish though with hook and line."

"Why was that?"

"They swam backward to keep the sweat out of their eyes. They could see where they had been but not where they were going. For this reason they would be past a baited hook before they could see it. You couldn't catch them from the shore or in shallow water either. They always stayed out in the center where the pond was deepest and coolest. You had to use a boat."

"How did you catch them?"

"This is the way I did it. I took two augers, a big one and a little one, and some limburger cheese and rowed out into the center of the pond. With the big auger I bored a hole in the bottom of the boat, right in the center. Then I smeared some of the cheese around the edge of the hole and sat back. The smell of the limburger cheese always attracted the fish. Swimming backward they came up tail first through the hole in the bottom of the boat."

"What was the little auger for?"

"Oh, I forgot to tell you about that. The back end of a boat always sets lower than the front end. I made a small hole at the back end so that any water that came in with the fish could run out. It's no fun to sit in a boat with your feet wet.

"There was always one danger in connection with sweat fishing. Sometimes the fish came up through the hole so fast that the boat was full in a hurry. When that happened I had to grab the oars and row to shore as fast as I could before it became overloaded and sank. As it was I had several close calls."

"Abe," Grandma's quiet voice broke in—"What time is it by your gold watch and chain? It seems to me it's way past Frank's bedtime."

Grandpa pulled his big, open-faced watch from his vest pocket. "Why so it is and past ours, too." Taking a small key from his lower vest pocket he slowly wound the watch: "Your grandmother is the best timepiece I ever had. Yet in all these years I have never been able to find out what makes her tick."

Not to be outdone Grandma retorted: "Your grandfather has to wind his watch every night but when it come to telling tall tales, he's always wound up!"

Water Auger

THE NEXT EVENING I HEADED BACK TO GRANDMA'S kitchen hoping to learn more about sweat fish.

"Guess what we had for supper tonight."

My grandparents looked up.

"Humming bird's tongues," said Grandpa with a twinkle in his eyes.

"I know," replied Grandma. "Your mother baked a shad. So did we. They were shipped up on ice from Kingston on the train this morning, the first of the season. I guess most everybody in the village ate shad tonight."

"Let me see," said Grandpa rubbing his beard: "This is Thursday. Your teacher is going to have some mighty smart pupils tomorrow."

"Why, Grandpa?"

"I've heard that fish are brain food."

"I had a second helping of shad. We have a spelldown in our grade tomorrow. Maybe I'll be the winner."

Both grandparents agreed that would be nice.

"Did you finish your sweat fish story last night?"

"Not quite. It won't take long. Then we'll give your grandmother a chance to beat us at dominoes."

"Before you begin your story, Abe, the popcorn is in the lard pail on the high shelf in the pantry where the mice can't get at it. If you'll fetch it, I'll have a pan full and all buttered by the time you're finished."

When Grandpa had resumed his seat and lit his pipe, he studied the ceiling a minute through the rising column of tobacco smoke and began: "Rather than risk the chance of having the boat sink from over-loading every time I went sweat-fishing with my big and little augers and limburger bait, I decided there must be a safer way. For a long time I couldn't come up with any ideas. Then one night when I was looking through our mail order catalog, I noticed in the section on tools that they sold different kinds of augers: carpenter's augers like the ones I used, ship's augers, post-hole augers, even sugar augers. I wondered if they could get me a water auger, one long enough to reach right down to the bottom of the ponds where the sweat fish lived. So I sent in my order and after a few weeks a long, slim package came. Sure enough it was my water auger with a foolproof guarantee.

"I went out into the woods and cut a slender straight hickory pole the same length as the water auger and pointed and notched it on one end. Then I rowed out into the middle of the pond where I knew there were sweat fish. Carefully leaning over the side of the boat, I bored several holes a few yards apart right down through the water to the bottom. Then every once in a while I rowed out and looked down into them. If any sweat fish, swimming backward, had hit one of these holes and dropped into it, they would be lying on the bottom stunned from their fall. All I had to do was reach down with my long spear-tipped pole and pick them out. It worked like a charm.

"When some of my neighbors found that I was using a water auger to catch sweat fish, they often came to borrow it. From then on we had all the fish we could eat.

"Did they taste anything like shad, Grandpa?"

"No, they were quite salty. More like salted mackerel. They were easy to keep, too. All you had to do was clean them, pack them in a keg and pour water over them. The natural salt in their bodies made a brine that preserved them."

"Do we still have sweat fish around here?"

"I don't rightly know. As the years went by, conditions changed in the way people lived and in the things they ate. My water auger was laid away and forgotten. So were the sweat fish. It is possible a few of them are still living in ponds and pot holes in the Catskills."

"Abe," Grandma broke in with a smile, "I wish you and Frank could go out and get some good live healthy sweat fish right now. The garden is drying up in this long hot spell and maybe putting some sweat fish in it for a few hours might do as much good as some rain."

Grandpa looked up and returned the smile. But before he could reply I asked: "How can you tell what ponds they're in?"

"The simplest way is to taste the water. If it's salty, it's the best sign they live there."

"Do you still have your water auger?"

"I haven't seen it for years. Sometime when you're in

the barn, look around. It might be laid up on one of the beams out of the way somewhere."

The tempting smell of popcorn and Grandmother's cheery, "Who is ready to play dominoes?" finished our story time.

More Fish Stories

"GRANDMA SAID I SHOULD COME IN AND KEEP YOU COMpany while she's in visiting with Mama."

Grandpa laid aside his paper. "I'm glad she did, Frank." He withdrew his carpet-slippered feet from the footstool and motioned for me to sit down.

"That story you told me about the sweat fish the other night was great."

"I'm glad you liked it. I guess there's no end to fish stories. There's something about things living under water that makes men's imaginations work overtime. We have stories about mermaids, sea serpents and the big fish that always seem to get away. I suppose the oldest fish story is the one about Jonah and the whale."

"Our teacher told us that the whale is an animal, not a fish. It has lungs instead of gills."

"That's true. But you can go fishing for a lot of things besides fish; there's sponge-fishing, lobster-fishing, whale-fishing, turtle-fishing, so I guess it is only natural to call it a fish story if what you catch comes out of the water."

"Do you know any more fish stories, Grandpa?"

He nodded, removed his spectacles, laid them on the

table beside the *Kingston Daily Freeman* and reached for his pipe. Caught up in the magic spell of fragrant tobacco, he leaned back, a faraway look came into his eyes, and he finally spoke:

"Many years ago I hauled a load of bluestone down to the docks at Wilbur on Rondout Creek below Kingston. We were unloading it so it could be taken aboard a barge and floated down the Hudson River to New York City. All of a sudden a heavy rainstorm came up. As we stood under a shed for protection it rained harder and harder until it became a cloudburst.

"The shad run was on and thousands of fish were making their yearly trip up from the ocean to lay their eggs in fresh water. From under that shed we noticed that some of the shad in trying to get ahead of the ones in front of them were swimming up the solid stream of falling rain instead of the creek. From what we found out later, the fish that went up into the cloud by mistake were afraid to come down after it stopped raining so they just stayed up there getting fat on the flying insects they caught as the cloud drifted about. This worked fine until a dry spell came on and the cloud evaporated. When this happened, they got so thirsty they had to come back to earth. One night when the moon was full they slid down on moonbeams and wriggled through the heavy dew to get a drink of water from whatever pond or stream was handy. The next day people found shad in places they had never seen them before, even in rail barrels and watering troughs."

"I'll bet the shad never made that mistake again, Grandpa."

"I'm sure they didn't."

"As long as Grandma hasn't come back yet, could I have another story before I go to bed? Tomorrow's Saturday."

Grandpa looked at his watch. "It's still early. I'll put my thinking cap on and see what I can come up with. And maybe your grandmother will be back before we're through to give you a treat."

At the moment a series of high-pitched screeches and yowls announced the beginning of a cat fight outside. Grandpa got up and pounded on the window.

"Sounds like some other tomcat has got in on old Tige's territory. Even if he has only three legs, Tige is the boss around here and I'll put my money on him every time."

As the sounds of the feline battle faded into the distance, Grandpa came back to his armchair and sat down: "I'll never forget the morning two winters ago when I went down to the barn and heard a cat meowing under the woodshed. When I called to it and Tige came out dragging that steel trap, I didn't realize his hind leg was frozen solid and he'd lose it."

"Gee, Grandpa, Clifford and I thought we might trap a weasel or skunk under there and sell the fur. We were sorry we caught our cat."

"It must have been a bad night for him. It hasn't slowed him down a bit though, he's a better fighter and mouser than most of 'em."

Grandpa paused to refill and light his pipe.

"Speaking of cats reminds me of the time I was fishing and a dog fish chased a catfish right out of the pond in front of me. The chase continued in full cry on land until the cat fish finally climbed a tree where its tormentor couldn't get at it. The dog fish sat there at the foot of the tree barking fiercely until I chased it back into the water. Then I waited for the poor trembling catfish to come down but it was too scared so I had to climb the tree and rescue it. By the time I carried it down to the ground, it had lost its fear and began to purr and ended up by licking my hand. I didn't have the heart to put it back in the pond where the dog fish would bother it again so I took it home with me and put it in the drinking trough in the barnyard. Late that afternoon when I was milking I heard a rustling noise in the straw beside me and looked down to see the catfish lay a mouse at my feet. It was so grateful that it hung around the barn for weeks catching mice until it was killed one night when one of the cows accidentally stepped on it."

It wasn't often that I was lucky enough to spend an evening alone with Grandpa. This night he seemed to be wound up and one story had led to another. When I thanked him, he smiled, looked at his watch again and said: "Your mother and grandmother are certainly making a night of it. We're always glad to have you come in, Frank. You give us something to think about and liven up our evenings. Now before you trot along to bed, let's see what we can find to eat. You fetch the cookie jar from the pantry, and I'll pull the dumbwaiter up from the cellar. I put a pitcher of milk on it when I came in from the barn and it'll be nice and cold by now."

Grandpa crossed the room, slid a panel to one side exposing a shaft within the wall. He pulled down on a rope that was looped over an iron pulley overhead until a cage came up with two shelves stocked with food that had to be kept cold. Two glasses of milk were quickly poured and the dumbwaiter retreated into the natural fifty degree temperature of the cellar below.

In spite of our small talk, the feast was soon over. As Grandpa turned again to the comfort of his pipe and paper, I said good-night and minutes later was sound asleep in bed.

Hoop Snakes

"GRANDPA, WHEN I WAS DRIVING THE COWS INTO THE barnyard this afternoon, I saw a snake crawl under the barn. It's the first one I've seen this year."

Grandpa put down his paper, laid his metal-rimmed spectacles aside and reached for his pipe. "These few warm days must have brought it out of hibernation."

"That's why I don't like to go down to the barn," said Grandma, looking up from her knitting. "They always seem to hang around there, and I'm afraid of them."

"Snakes are good to have around the buildings," continued Grandpa, "because they catch rats and mice. They can get into places where a cat can't go. What did it look like, Frank?"

"It was quite long and kind of light-colored with spots on it."

"Sounds like a milk snake or spotted adder to me. They do a lot of good around the place. Don't worry, it won't bother you."

"Why do they call it a milk snake? Does it drink milk?"

"No, it doesn't, but people used to think it did. If the

cow didn't give as much milk as usual, people got the notion that the snake they saw around the barn had milked her. So the idea got around that it drank milk, and they gave it that name. It prefers to eat mice so it hangs around barns where there are always plenty of them. They get quite tame if you leave them alone."

"Did you ever have a pet snake, Grandpa?"

"Well, not exactly. I helped a snake out of trouble once and it followed me home, but I didn't really make a pet out of it."

"What kind of trouble could a snake get into?"

"That's a long story and it happened a long time ago."

"Abe," Grandma broke in as she stood up, "if you two are going to keep on talking about snakes, I'm going over to the other side of the house to visit with Nellie again. Marion will be practicing her piano lesson and I'll find out how she's getting along. Your mother tells me, Frank, that your sister practices every night while you're in here listening to your grandfather's stories."

"That's right. But I'd rather listen to Grandpa."

As Grandma disappeared through the pantry doorway, Grandpa leaned back in his armchair, puffed on his pipe and leisurely examined the ceiling.

"Of all the snakes in the Catskills, the hoop snake is the queerest. It travels by putting its tail in its mouth and rolling along like a hoop. It has a poison stinger near the end of its tail that it uses to strike its prey."

"Are they dangerous?"

"You bet they are. They usually don't bother people,

but when they have young with them they may turn on you. I suppose they think their little ones are in danger and are trying to protect them. I remember once I was hoeing out in the potato field when all of a sudden I heard a humming noise and looked up to see a big hoop snake coming toward me. I jumped out of the way just in time, but the stinger hit the handle of the hoe and knocked it out of my hand. Before the hooper could turn around and come back I had jumped over the stone wall and it couldn't get at me. It gave up and rolled away with about twenty of its spotted babies. They were about the size of a hoop from a nail keg and cute little things. When I went back to the potato field, the hoe handle was beginning to swell up from the poison stinger. By the next day it was as big as a fence post and was warm as if it had a fever. I never could use it after that. A few days later I saw the mother and her litter out on a sunny hillside in the pasture. The young ones were rolling in and out of the hoop made by their mother's body as if they were playing a game."

"What about the snake you helped out of trouble?"

"That's another story. One day while I was walking through the woods looking for a pine tree to work up into shingles for roofing a new cowshed, I heard a thumping noise and sneaked up behind a bush to see what it was all about. A big hoop snake had its stinger stuck in the trunk of a sugar maple tree and was thrashing around trying to pull itself loose. It must have missed whatever it was after and hit the tree instead. As long as the stinger was fast in the tree, I knew it couldn't hurt me so I walked up close to it. When it saw me it quieted down, raised its head about three feet off the ground and began to sway back and forth like it was doing a dance. I knew the only poison it had was in the stinger on its tail so I held out my hand and it licked it with its little forked tongue. As I turned to go it looked at me so pitiful-like with tears rolling down its cheeks that I didn't have the heart to leave it there to die. I decided to take a chance. I drove my iron wedge into the maple and split the tree open far enough so the snake could pull its stinger out. When it was free, it came to me again and licked my hand, and when I started home it put its tail in its mouth and rolled along with me. For a long time it lived under the barn and never gave us a bit of trouble. It became very playful and would do all kinds of hoop-spinning tricks.

"I still hadn't found a pine tree to make the shingles for my cattle shed so I went back to the woods one day to look again. When I passed the maple that the hoop snake had hit with its stinger, the tree was dead and had swelled up to almost double its size. When I saw this, I got an idea!

"I cut down a small pine tree and dragged it back to the barn. It took only a few minutes to cut it up into the right lengths for the shingles. Then I called the hoop snake out from under the barn and picked it up. It liked the feel of my warm hands. I pushed the stinger into each section of the soft pine wood and the poison took effect at once. The pieces began to swell right before my eyes until they were as big around as a full-sized log. The next day I split them up and had a new roof on the shed in no time."

"That was a great idea, Grandpa."

"It seemed so at the time. The more I thought about it the more I was sure that I had found an easy way to make a lot of money: just bring in a bunch of poles, inject hoop snake poison into them and when they had swelled up to saw log size sell them to the mill for lumber."

"Did you do it?"

"Not quite. Before I got around to it, summer had passed into fall and the rainy season came on. The rainwater on the cow shed roof leeched all of the poison out of the shingles and the wood shrank down to its original size, letting in plenty of daylight and rain. That's how I found out that my scheme wouldn't work."

"That's too bad. Do we still have hoop snakes around here?"

"I haven't seen any in years. When woodchucks moved in, the hoop snakes moved out. For some reason they were deadly afraid of woodchucks. Even the skin of a woodchuck nailed up on a barn would scare them away. As the land was cleared of trees, more wood-chucks appeared and hoop snakes became scarcer and scarcer. I don't know where you could find one any more. But if you want to see what their stinger looked like, take a good look at any old rooster. The spur on the leg of a rooster and the stinger of a full-grown hoop snake were so much alike I don't believe you could tell the difference."

Footsteps sounded and Grandma came through the pantry doorway with a plate of molasses cookies in her hand. "These are from Nellie," she said looking at Grandpa. "She's one of the best cooks and housekeepers around. I'm glad Levi gave up his bachelor notions after he met her at the Glenford church social."

"So am I," responded Grandpa heartily as he laid a hand on my shoulder and with the other one helped himself to a cookie.

"If you two are through with your snake stories, I'll let you stay long enough, Frank, to have a glass of milk with one of your mother's cookies. Then off to bed with you."

Plowing

"YOUR GRANDFATHER IS AT A CHURCH MEETING," Grandma said when I found her sitting alone in her kitchen one evening in May. "I'm afraid he won't be home until long after your bedtime. I guess you can go one night without a story, can't you, Frank?"

"Why don't you tell me one, Grandma?"

"I'm not given to spinning yarns. Any story I might tell wouldn't hold a candle to the tall tales your Grandfather knows."

"Think hard, Grandma. Didn't anything ever happen to Grandpa that he forgot to tell me about?"

"Well, let me see! Your grandfather has been a church deacon for a great many years. Oh! Yes! A funny thing happened when your father and mother still lived upstairs over the store.

"One spring our daughter, your Aunt Elizabeth, who lives in Brooklyn, wrote and asked us to come down and pay her a visit. Your grandfather said that I should go but that he'd stay home to look after the place and do the farm work. It was a long trip to take alone, but I wrote that I'd be there on a certain day."

"How did you get there?"

"I went down to the railroad station and took the Ulster and Delaware to Kingston. There I changed to the West Shore Railroad and rode 90 miles south to Hoboken, New Jersey; then across the Hudson River on the ferry boat to New York City. Your aunt met me at the dock and we rode over to Brooklyn on the street car. It was a long day's trip. When I came back three weeks later, the neighbors told me this story:

"Grandfather wasn't used to batching it, and after a while he lost track of the days of the week. One morning he got up early as usual, did the chores, took a tub bath in the kitchen, shaved and put on his Sunday go-to-meeting clothes. As an elder of the church he had to get there early to open it up. When he walked down the street, he cut quite a fine figure with his standup collar, his swallowtail coat and stovepipe hat. He hadn't gone far before one of the neighbors stopped him and asked where he was going all dressed up on Saturday morning. Grandfather allowed as how he was going to church, and besides it wasn't Saturday, it was Sunday. Another neighbor came up and asked who had died. He thought Grandfather was going to a funeral. While they were talking Grandfather looked around and could plainly see that everybody else was dressed in regular everyday work clothes so he finally agreed that he must be mistaken about its being Sunday.

"When your grandfather once makes up his mind, however, he doesn't change it easily. After going to all that trouble to put on his Sunday clothes, he had no intention of changing back. He had some plowing to do so he just went on back to the barn and yoked up a pair of young oxen he had broken in. He had a new piece of cleared land that he wanted to turn under and that's what he was going to do. Still dressed in his Sunday best, he pulled the plow up on the stoneboat, hooked the oxen to it and away they went.

"Soon the oxen were leaning into the yoke plowing the furrows in even lines across the field. Back and forth they went. Then he looked down and saw that his polished leather boots were getting muddy as he walked in the freshly turned soil. He was peeved at himself for getting his days mixed up. Before he realized what had happened, the plow struck something hard and the oxen stopped in their tracks. They had walked around a low elm stump that stood at the edge of the field and had driven the point of the plow deep into the hard green wood.

"Your grandfather is a big and strong man, so he began to yank and pull on the plow handles to get it loose. But it wouldn't work. Then he cracked his whip and yelled hoping the oxen would split the stump in two and free the plow that way. Nothing happened, even though the oxen pulled and strained until they were almost laying forward on the ground. Finally your grandfather laid the lash on the oxen, and they tried again. This time the wood parted, and the stump split wide open. Grandfather held onto the handles and walked right through the open stump behind the plow. When he got to the other side, the stump snapped shut behind him like a big wooden trap and caught his long coattails in its grip.

"By this time your grandfather was really mad. No

fool stump was going to get the best of him! So he hung onto the plow handles for all he was worth and yelled at the oxen. He'd get those coattails out by main strength or know the reason why!

"When the coattails pulled tight, the oxen really dug in and made the dirt fly. And your grandfather was so stubborn he'd never let go. Something had to give . . . and it did! The ox yoke broke in two under the strain. And at the same time the buttons popped off the front of the coat. Without so much as a single look behind him, your grandfather shucked off the coat and drove the oxen home. The elm stump had got the best of him in a tug of war. I went out and picked up the buttons, but he never would go back and try to get the coat

loose. He left it laying there on the ground with the swallowtails still caught in the stump until the wood finally rotted entirely away. Then he went out, picked it up and brought it home. I brushed it and ironed it and sewed the buttons back on and your grandfather wore it again to church every Sunday."

"They must have made clothes of mighty good stuff in those days, Grandma."

"Yes, they did, Frank. You can't buy goods like that anymore. Now it's time you were on your way to bed. But before you go help yourself to an oatmeal cookie from the jar and I'll pour you a glass of milk."

"That was a peach of a story, Grandma. Maybe sometime if Grandpa isn't here you'll tell me another."

"I don't claim to be able to tell stories like your grandfather, but I haven't lived with him all these years without having a few unusual things to talk about."

Churning

GRANDMA WAS SITTING AT THE OPEN DOOR CHURNING as I walked into her kitchen. The up and down motion of the dasher made a splashing sound like waves against the side of a boat. She was beating time to the hymn she was softly singing.

"Come in, Frank. I'll have a treat for you pretty soon."

Grandpa's footsteps sounded on the back steps and he came in from the barn, his chores done for the day.

"Liza, why don't you let this young man try his muscle and give you a breathing spell?"

"I will one of these times. The butter is starting to come so I'm almost through. It's so peaceful sitting here watching the night settle down on Overlook Mountain."

"Yes, it's a beautiful evening." He took off his boots, put on his slippers, lifted a dipper of water from the pail to the washbasin and washed his hands.

Grandma finished her churning, ladled out the butter into a wooden bowl and dipped up a pitcher of buttermilk from the churn. She took three glasses from the cupboard. "Buttermilk doesn't come any fresher, and there's plenty. Frank, I know you like a spoonful of sugar in yours. Wait on yourself but take only one. After I work the butter and salt it, I'll join you."

Grandpa, comfortably seated in his armchair, sipped his buttermilk and smacked his lips. It was easy to see that he was in a pleasant frame of mind.

"I usually had to do the churning when I was a boy. In warm weather it was done in the springhouse where the tin pans of milk and cream were set to keep them fresh and sweet.

"One summer day I had just put a batch of cream in and started to churn when the paddle broke on the wooden dasher. My father, that would be your great-grandfather, had a workbench and toolbox in one side of the woodshed so I took the broken part there to mend it. Since I would be back in a little while, I didn't bother to put the cover on the churn. When I got back, I heard a splashing sound and looked into the churn and there sat a big, fat bullfrog kicking away with his long hind legs. The surface of the milk was covered with butter.

"The bullfrog looked up at me, winked an eye and sat still. He seemed quite tame so I reached in and lifted him out. Since he had done the churning for me, I put him in a pail and went out and caught a couple of grasshoppers for him to eat. I figured he lived in the spring or in the brook that flowed from it, so I dropped him back into the water where he dove to the bottom and disappeared.

"The next time churning day came around, I got everything ready as usual. As I was about to put the dasher in, I heard a noise and here came the bullfrog swimming over the surface of the spring with a powerful breast stroke. Before I knew what he was up to, he climbed out of the water, jumped up on the workbench and into the open churn. As soon as he hit the cream, he started to splash around, kicking his big webbed hind feet like fancy green paddles and had the butter coming in short order.

"The bullfrog took over the churning all that summer and fall and seemed to enjoy it. Of course I always fed him a few grasshoppers or crickets for helping me. Finally when the weather began to get cold, he didn't show up any more so I figured he had gone into hibernation."

"I'll bet you really missed his help, Grandpa, when you had to do the churning again."

"I'll say I did. That bullfrog really had me spoiled. Well, anyway, the weeks and months went by and I kind of forgot about the whole thing. Then one warm sunny day the following April when the grass in the pasture had turned green and the red-winged blackbirds were calling along the brook, a deep-voiced frog began to bellow like a faraway bull. I went down to the springhouse and there was a huge bullfrog. It sat perfectly still when I came near it. I leaned over and scratched its back and its bellow turned into a contented throaty rumbling. My churning frog had reported for duty.

"With the bullfrog back to do the churning, I began to worry about the things that might happen to my helper. The chance that it might be speared by a neighbor farm boy or caught by a heron or mink worried me. To be sure that anyone seeing it would know that it was no ordinary frog, I painted a red bow tie on its broad yellow throat.

"The days passed by and it was fall again, and still the big friendly bullfrog, handsome in its red tie, appeared regularly to do the churning and get its reward of grasshoppers and crickets. It became so fat and lazy that several times it was nearly stepped on by the cattle that came to drink at the edge of the spring.

"One late afternoon I drove the cows up the lane from the pasture. They stopped below the spring as usual to get a drink. Suddenly Old Bess snorted, jumped back, and started to bellow excitedly. She tried to bolt past me and get back to the pasture but I headed her off and drove her into the barnyard with the rest of the herd where she kept on jumping around. When it came her turn to be milked, I had to put her in the stanchion to make her stand still. It was then I noticed that she had developed a bad case of hiccoughs. I could see right away that I was wasting my time, so I gave up trying to milk her. And rather than take a chance on having her get down sick out in the pasture during the night, I kept her in the barn while I turned the rest out.

"By morning Old Bess had calmed down and seemed to be over her mysterious attack, so I started to milk her. To my surprise I couldn't get any at all. Instead all she let down in the pail was streams of pure, warm, melted butter.

"After the milking was over, I went down to the spring and called and looked everywhere for the bullfrog, but it didn't show up. I never did see it again."

"What do you think happened to it, Grandpa?"

"I figured that Old Bess had swallowed it when she came up to drink and that's what upset her the night before. Now exerything seemed to be all right and the frog from force of habit was doing the churning as usual, but this time it was an inside job.

"This arrangement seemed to agree with Old Bess. She held her head high and acted like she was proud of her fame as the only Catskill Mountain cow that ever gave butter. The only change I ever noticed in her eating habits was her sudden liking for crickets and grasshoppers.

"And I'm sure that the bullfrog was happy too, because now he had a full-time job churning butter with no winter layoff."

"Grandpa, did that really happen?"

He smiled, stroked his beard and looked silently at Grandma.

She merely said: "You should know by now that your grandfather has a wonderful imagination. Don't be surprised at anything that happens in one of his stories."

Adventure With a Bear

THEY WERE SITTING AT THE KITCHEN TABLE AS I AP-
peared through the pantry doorway. Grandpa motioned
me to a chair and said: "You're just in time, Frank.
Your grandmother is telling me some news, and you
can hear it too."

Grandma smiled and nodded. "I'll repeat what I
just started to tell your grandfather. Mrs. Row and
Mrs. Avery and their children went after highbush
huckleberries this morning in the O'Neil swamp. They
split up and each one took a separate clump of bushes
to pick. They were going to have a kind of a race to
see who could get the first two-quart pail full. So everybody got busy and it was quiet except for the rustle of
the bushes.

"All at once Mrs. Avery let out a scream and came
running back to the rest of them yelling: "A bear! Run
for your lives!" They all dropped their pails and got
out of there as fast as they could.

"When they got up to the old wood road on the
ridge, Mrs. Avery told them she had been picking away
when the clump of bushes she was working on began to
shake. She thought it was one of the children so she

didn't say anything. As she worked around the side, she saw what she first thought was a tall man wearing a dark coat picking berries. He looked at her, dropped down on all fours and plunged into the bushes. That was when she screamed and ran. They didn't dare go back."

We looked at Grandpa. "We very seldom see bears around here anymore," he said. "It was probably a male who had wandered down out of the mountains. He happened to find the huckleberry patch just about when they did. And he was probably as scared as Mrs. Avery was. I'll bet he ran a mile. They were lucky it wasn't a she-bear with cubs. A female with her young is always dangerous. I wouldn't worry. We probably won't have another bear reported around here for years."

"I'm glad I wasn't there," Grandma said. "Between bears and snakes, I'll pick my huckleberries at the store."

"If the womenfolk are afraid to go back, maybe some of the big boys'll be brave enough to go get the pails and fill them. It's too bad to let the raccoons and birds pick all of them." With this sensible conclusion, Grandpa stood up and walked toward his armchair.

"That was a good bear story, Grandma, but it was too short because the bear ran away."

"I've no mind to compete with your grandfather with his tall tales. I'll get a glass of milk and a cookie for you and go on with my knitting and he can amuse you."

"How about it, Grandpa?"

"Well, Frank, we might as well make this a night for

bear stories, and I'll tell you what happened to me once when I was a young man living back on the farm:

"One summer day Jim Slater, a neighbor, and I were up in the mountains exploring new country when we ran across a large cave at the base of a cliff. The opening was big enough for a man to walk into. We looked in but it was pitch black in there so we couldn't tell how far back the hole went.

"We sat down to rest, and the more we talked about what might be in it, the more excited Jim got. Could Indians have lived in it before white men settled the country? Could white hunters have used it for a shelter? Could robbers have hidden their stolen treasure in it and never came back to get it? Maybe wild animals used it for a den!

"Jim was all for lighting a pine knot as a torch and going in to look around. I said there might be loose rocks ready to fall from the ceiling. Or it could even be a panther's or bear's den. But Jim wouldn't give up the idea and said he'd go in alone and look around. So finally to get it over with I told him to go ahead or we wouldn't get home before dark. No snooping around in spooky caves for me.

"Jim went over to a fallen pitch pine and pulled the stub of a branch loose from the rotting trunk. He built a little fire on the ground and held the stub in it until he had it blazing. Then with the smoky torch held above his head he laughed and said: "Now I feel like a caveman who is going home," and disappeared from sight into the dark opening among the rocks.

Everything was quiet. I had an uneasy feeling because I didn't like the chance he was taking. A few minutes went by and then, the stillness was broken by a fearful yell. Seconds later Jim rushed out with blood streaming down his face.

"Run," he screamed as he dashed past me, and I turned and ran after him as fast as my legs would carry me. It was then I saw what an awful condition he was in. All of the hair was gone from the top of his head, as though he had been scalped by an Indian on the warpath, and he was bleeding badly. We ran a short way and suddenly Jim stopped and sank to the ground like a big rag doll. He had fainted dead away from the shock and the loss of blood. I had to do something quick to keep him from bleeding to death.

"Just then a weasel, excited from smelling the fresh blood, came out of a pile of rocks and ran up to us. I killed it with a stick. Taking out my jackknife, I hastily skinned it, trimmed the warm hide into the proper shape and stretched in into place on Jim's head to stop the flow of blood. Then from a nearby thornapple tree I cut a sharp thorn and using it as a needle, and with a thread pulled out of my shirt, sewed the skin in place. When he finally came to, a patch of brown weasel fur covered the bare spot on the top of Jim's head.

"After he had recovered enough to talk, he told me what had happened in the cave. He had worked his way around several big rocks on the cave floor. Then he tripped over a stick and fell forward upon a warm, furry thing that let out its breath with a loud 'woof'. The torch dropped from Jim's hand and the flame went out. Jim let out a terrified yell as he jumped to his feet in the darkness. A frightened bear roused from its sleep, rose up on its hind legs and took a swipe at Jim. Its open paw hit him a glancing blow alongside the head and spun him around. Like a boxer the bear swung its other paw and its open claws tore the skin and hair off his head. Before the angry beast could close in for the deadly bear hug, Jim turned toward the dimly lit mouth of the cave and got away. Luckily for both of us the bear did not follow.

"In a short time the skin took hold and grafted perfectly in place, and Jim ended up with a fine full head of pretty brown hair. It saved him money, too. He never needed a haircut after that. The natural full length of the weasel's fur was only a half inch and it never grew any longer.

"The following fall a queer thing happened. Jim began to turn gray about the temples. Gradually the white spread through the hair over the whole top of his head. Folks thought that this sudden grayness was caused by the terrible fright he had had by being scalped by the bear earlier in the year. But the next spring his hair began to turn a rich brown color again. Then he knew that the grafted weasel skin was simply going through its regular seasonal change . . . the brown of summer and the white of winter.

"This went on for a number of years until one fall Jim's hair only turned partly white. Later on he found out why. We had an open winter with a number of unusually warm spells that melted the snow away and it felt like spring was coming. After that the neighbors kept a close watch of Jim's head, claiming they could

predict what kind of winter we were going to have just by looking at his hair. He became a kind of human weather station."

"Gee! That was a dandy, scary story."

Grandma looked up and cleared her throat. "I must admit your grandfather tells a much better story than I do. But then you must bear in mind, he's had much more practice."

Good Hunting

"I LIKE YOUR HUNTING STORIES, GRANDPA. WHEN YOU go out in the mountains you never know what's going to happen next."

"You're quite right, Frank. That's what makes it interesting. Hunting in the Catskills wasn't always the failure it was the day I met up with the cherry-tree buck and the panther. I remember one time I bagged more game with just one shot than two men could carry home."

"How in the world could you do that?"

Before he could reply, Grandma's voice broke in: "With a good day's work behind him and a good supper inside him, your grandfather can think up all sorts of unlikely things to amuse you. And while he is at it, I'll bring you a glass of milk and a cookie."

Grandpa looked at Grandma and smiled as she headed for the pantry. "I've wasted a lot of powder and lead in my time. But I've made some good shots too. Sometimes I was just plain lucky. Anyway it happened like this:

"When I was young I trapped muskrats and mink every fall. This one year I got out my traps and went down to the Beaverkill where I set out a line of them. I got pretty tired wading around in the mud and water in my hip boots, at the same time trying to keep my gun from getting wet, so I was glad when I was finally finished and on my way home. I had just climbed up a steep bank above a deep waterhole when a duck flew up out of the reeds. I took a quick shot at it and missed.

"Stopping to reload, I heard a disturbance in the brush up on the hillside above me. I looked up to see two full-grown black bears racing down the slope right at me. As I hastily dropped a big charge of powder into the gun and rammed a bullet down the barrel after it, I saw that the bears were going to separate and come around opposite sides of a large, thin-edged rock, which lay like the prow of a ship just in front of me. In a flash I saw I was in a tight spot. If I shot one bear, the other would be on me before I could reload. So making a lightning-quick decision, I pulled up my gun and aimed, not at one of the bears, but at the front of the rock, and fired just as the animals came around each side. The bullet hit the knife-like edge and split in two. Each half was deflected just enough to hit one of the bears in the head, and both dropped dead on the spot.

"The recoil of the overloaded gun kicked me with so much force that I was knocked backwards off the bank and into the pool, hitting a beaver, which had just come up for air, and breaking its neck. As I scrambled out of the water, I felt a slippery noose coiling around my arm. I yanked it off and threw it up on the bank. It was a large eel.

"At this point several wild geese hit the water in front of me, neatly threaded on the ramrod of my gun. In my haste to reload, I had forgotten to withdraw the hickory ramrod from the barrel so when I fired at the bears it shot out ahead of the bullet. It had glanced off the face of the rock and flown up into the air spearing five geese that were part of a flock passing overhead.

"Now I felt something wriggling in my boots. Reaching in I brought out a mink from one and a muskrat from the other. I knocked their heads together and tossed them up on the bank. About this time I realized that my pants were sagging dangerously from the weight of the water in the pockets. I grabbed them but I was a second too late. My suspender buttons let go from the strain on them. The two front buttons flew up and killed a pair of gray squirrels that were playing tag around the trunk of a chestnut tree. The back buttons connected with a black duck that was circling to land in the pool behind me and a wild turkey that was flying across the swamp.

"And believe it or not, in the pockets of my pants as I pulled them up out of the water I found enough bullheads to make a nice mess of fish for supper.

"Maybe you could call it luck, but with that one shot I had fish, flesh, fowl, furs, and enough goose feathers to fill a pair of pillows, not to mention a bath which I didn't need . . . you see it was only Thursday."

"Grandpa, I don't see how two men could carry all that game home in one trip. Besides, you were alone."

"That's right. I went back and got two men to help. We loaded it all in the wagon."

Grandpa knocked the ashes out of his pipe and looked at his watch. "I didn't realize it was so late. I hope I didn't bore you, Liza."

Grandma yawned and put away her knitting. "No, Abe, you didn't. But I got the cold shivers when you mentioned the eel. I know it's a fish, but it looks so much like a black snake I wouldn't touch one with a ten-foot pole."

I stood up, looked in wonderment at my hero-grand-father, said 'Good-night' and went through the pantry and up the stairs to dream of the single shot that had come echoing down through the years.

Sidehill Gougers

As I made my way through the pantry and into her kitchen, Grandma was cracking hickory nuts and picking out the meats. She turned toward me.

"Your grandfather is out on the front porch trying to cool off. The mosquitoes were too much for me so I came in. Besides I'm baking a cake for the church social Friday so I have to get things ready for it."

"I don't mind a few little mosquitoes if Grandpa will tell me a story."

"I think you'd better get the citronella bottle off the shelf, Frank, and rub some on your face and neck or you'll get eaten up."

Protected by the citronella, I went through the parlor to the porch where I could see the glow of Grandpa's pipe as he slowly took a puff.

"I wondered if you'd be around to help me fight off the mosquitoes," he said as I opened the screen door and stepped outside. "Draw up that chair, and we'll see if the smoke will keep them away from both of us. I guess you don't need my help, though. I smell citronella."

"Grandma told me to put some on."

"That's good. There's a little breeze out here but not enough to blow them away. What did you do today?"

"A few of us played ball on the school grounds until it was time to go for the cows. I had a hard time finding them. They were in the upper pasture standing in a cedar thicket. When I drove them out, they didn't want to go down the hill."

"At this time of the year when flies and mosquitoes are bad, cattle like to go up in the hills where there's usually a breeze that helps keep them away. Be careful not to hurry cows down a steep hill. They're so big and heavy they fall easily and might break their legs. Let them follow the zigzag trails they've made. Now sheep and goats are more sure-footed but sidehill gougers are the best of all."

"Sidehill gougers? What're they?"

"They're animals that live up in the mountains. Their legs are longer on the downhill side so they can run around on the steep slopes just as easily as ordinary animals do on level ground.

"Let me see. Your brother Clifford is left-handed and you're right-handed. Sidehill gougers are like that too, only they're either left-legged or right-legged. The ones with longer legs on the left side always travel clockwise. If their legs are longer on the right-hand side, they have to go counter-clockwise or they'll tip over and fall down the mountain. So you see they spend their lives going around in circles.

"What do they do if they meet?"

"They turn out enough so they can pass or simply leap over each other. They're about the size of goats and have very sharp hoofs that gouge out paths in the mountain sides. They can travel with ease wherever the ground is on a slant, on hillsides as well as mountains. But they can't walk on level ground because of the difference in the length of their legs."

"Then they never come down in the valleys?"

"Only if driven there by fire or perhaps by dogs. If they ever do get on level ground, they run in small circles so they won't tip over. It's the same idea as riding a bicycle in a circle. You lean toward the center as you go around, and as long as you keep going you don't fall. If a gouger stops running when it's on flat ground, it falls down and can't get up again. I once found a gouger laying on its side out in a field I was plowing."

"How did it get there?"

"I don't know. Anyway, there it was. I tried to pick it up and stand it on its feet, but it kicked so hard I was afraid its sharp hoofs would cut me to pieces. I didn't want it to die there, so I plowed a furrow from the base of a hill that was close by. Then with a forked stick I pushed it so it could get its longer legs into the bottom of the furrow and stand up. It was so scared it went out there as fast as greased lightning and I could hardly see it for the dirt it kicked up."

"That must have been mighty fast."

"Yes, they could run faster than a bullet from the old-fashioned muzzle-loaders we used when I was young. I did manage to hit one once, but I ruined my gun doing it."

"How did you hit it if it could go faster than a bullet?"

"I bent my gun barrel to the left in a curve. Then I went up into the mountains where they traveled clockwise. When the gougers ran away, I fired my gun in the opposite direction. Somewhere on the other side of the mountain the hard-headed old leader of the herd ran into the bullet and flattened it as thin as a dime. He must have hit it with one of his horns and it didn't hurt him a bit. I doubt if he even got a headache out of it. That was the last time I ever tried to shoot a sidehill gouger."

"Were they good to eat?"

"No, their meat was as tough as tripe. But their fur was good. In the winter it was thick and warm and curly. Funny thing about sidehill gougers. They never shed their fur in the spring like other animals. Instead, when warm weather came on, they molted like a snake does and got rid of their entire old skin with the fur still on it."

"How was that, Grandpa?"

"Well, a snake grows a new skin under the old one. Then it crawls under something and the old skin is pushed off, something like you take off your stockings at night before going to bed. Now with the sidehill gouger, it was a little different. It swallowed air and blew itself up like a balloon. Not like a full balloon. The pressure inside made it swell up just enough so the dry, old outside skin split down the back. It simply jumped out of the stuffy old winter skin and there it was, covered with the brand new one complete with lighter fur for summer. In the fall it molted its summer suit and stepped out in a warmer one for winter.

"People used to go up in the mountains and collect the skins during the molting season. They had them tanned and made into overcoats, bed covers, rugs and even lap robes for sleighs."

"Can we go out some day and look for the old skins, Grandpa? And see some of the sidehill gougers?"

"I don't get around in the mountains like I used to, Frank, and I haven't seen any gougers for a long time. They aren't common like they used to be. One winter many years ago a January thaw set in and lasted so long the sidehill gougers thought it was springtime. They shed their winter skins. Then the weather changed, winter set in again and the temperature dropped to blow zero and they froze to death. But in some places on the hillsides you can still see the trails they made. The cows use them for their paths."

"Maybe some day I'll see one."

"I hope so. Years ago I had a fur cap and a pair of mittens made from sidehill gouger's skin. Maybe your Grandmother will look in the cedar chest and see if they're still around.

"But I think right now we'd better go in the house and let the mosquitoes go to bed."

Soft Soap Satan

GRANDMA AND GRANDPA WERE TALKING OVER PLANS for making a batch of soft soap when I entered their kitchen one pleasant autumn evening. The wood ashes that had been saved from the kitchen stove had been sifted and put in the leaching barrel outside and the lye water had been drained off at the bottom. This in turn had been boiled down until it was now a strong liquid. Grandma for weeks had saved and strained grease and stored it in crocks in the cool cellar. Now the time had come for Grandpa to hang the big iron kettle on a tripod of poles out of doors. Simmering over a hot bed of hardwood coals the next day, the messy hot grease and the fiery lye would combine to make a supply of mild soft soap.

Grandpa stood up and looked out of the window. The peak of Overlook Mountain to the north was still bathed in sunlight. He reached for his hat and turned toward me.

"Let's get the jump on tomorrow, Frank. There's just enough light left for us to set up the poles and hang the kettle."

It was fun to work with Grandpa. He always made

me feel big and important. We finished the set-up and even carried out the firewood from the shed before it was too dark to see.

"Liza, I don't see how I could get along without Frank," Grandpa said when we came back into the kitchen.

"He is a big help," replied Grandma. "You two are good for each other. Can't you see yourself growing up all over again?"

Grandpa nodded. "We need grandchildren to keep us young. When I'm with Frank, I forget I'm seventy-one years old."

Grandma looked up contentedly from her knitting and smiled. "Your father lived to be eighty-eight, Abe, so maybe we'd better say you're only seventy-one years young."

It was growing late so I spoke up: "Grandpa, are you going to tell me a story tonight?"

Without replying, he turned around and went through the familiar ceremony of filling and lighting his pipe, then seated himself leisurely in his armchair. Several puffs later he began:

"My father told me this story many years ago. He was born in 1812 and as a boy heard all about the digging of the Erie Canal across New York State from the Hudson River to Buffalo. When it was finished in 1825, settlers going west could travel by water to Lake Erie and then by steamboat across the Great Lakes to such far-off places as Detroit, Michigan, and Chicago, in Illinois. This was cheaper and easier than going by land. The canal boats were usually pulled by mules that walked alongside the canal on special tow paths."

"Why didn't they use horses, Grandpa?"

"Mules cost less, ate less and didn't need the care that horses would. There was a farmer near the canal who had a young black mule that balked at doing this kind of work, or any kind of work for that matter. He was so mean, he would kick and bite and even chase dogs and people. If kept in a stable, he would kick it to pieces. Everybody around knew Satan, the black mule that was always getting into trouble. Finally the farmer became so disgusted with this good-for-nothing animal that he figured he might have to shoot him.

"But before he had a chance to make up his mind, he had to take a trip to town with a load of hay. Satan was put out to pasture. On that same day the farmer's wife made a batch of soft soap out in the back yard. She had the work about done when she heard Satan squealing. She looked up in time to see him kick the pasture gate to pieces and come charging after her. She ran into the house and locked the door for safety. Satan galloped around the yard smashing things to smithereens. Then he noticed the big tub of warm soap. This was something new to him. He smelled it, then tasted it. It must have tasted good because he began to drink it and didn't stop until he had almost emptied the tub.

"After Satan had finished, he let out a couple of happy hee-haws and walked over to the nearest tree and took a nap in the shade. When the farmer came home later, the mule shyly came over to be petted and followed him about like a big friendly dog. The farmer couldn't understand what had come over the animal until his wife told him what had happened.

"The mule had soft-soaped himself into such good humor that there never again was a mean streak in his whole body. From that day on, he was gentle and playful and became everybody's pet. He was especially fond of children."

"That was a good story, Grandpa. Did Satan go back to pulling canal boats?"

"Yes, after that he seemed anxious to earn his keep. But the story isn't ended yet.

"The farmer soon noticed that Satan's black hide broke out into a lather every time it rained. He didn't give any thought to it until one Sunday morning when he started to shave and found he had run out of shaving soap. So he took a cup of warm water and went out and poured it on Satan's hide. He stirred up the wet spot with his shaving brush and worked up a good lather. It softened up his beard better than any shaving soap he had ever used. He told his wife about it. The next day being Monday she poured warm water over Satan and caught the soapsuds in the washtub. Her wash came out cleaner and whiter than ever before. This made Satan more popular than ever. He never did get all of the soft soap out of his system."

"Grandpa, I guess Satan paid back for the trouble he had been."

"Yes, everybody was happy with the way things turned out. This went on for years with enough free lather and soapsuds for the whole neighborhood until Satan became too old to work any more. Then the farmer sold him to a barber who used him as his lather supply as long as the mule lived."

As the story ended, Grandma put down her knitting and started toward the pantry, a sure sign of something good to eat in the offing.

"Abe," she said with a big smile, "of the thousands of people who have gotten a kick out of that mule story for the past eighty years, I wonder how many realized that a little soft soap in life goes a long, long ways and never does anybody any harm."

Shotgun Farming

"YOU'RE HERE EARLY TONIGHT, FRANK," GRANDMA RE-
marked as I entered her kitchen through the pantry
doorway. "Your Grandfather is out in the garden digging holes for a row of potatoes. I've just finished cutting up some that have sprouted."

"I'll take them out to him."

"That will be fine. Thank you."

I took the pan and went outside through the woodshed. Grandpa had just finished digging and was turning back to the house with his hoe.

"Here are the potatoes, Grandpa. I'll drop them for
you if you want me to."

"That'll be a big help. One piece to a hole, and I'll
follow you and cover them."

"Why do potatoes have eyes?"

"Well, that's a good question. When a potato starts
to grow, sprouts come out of its eyes and turn toward
the light so maybe it uses its eyes to see with. And by
the way, if it wasn't so late, we might ask your Grandmother to cut up an onion and you could drop a slice
in each hole."

"What for?"

"Since onions make our eyes water, I wonder if they wouldn't make the potatoes' eyes water so they'd keep on growing if we had a dry spell."

"Shall I go ask Grandma for one?"

"I guess not tonight. It's so late we'll have to hurry or we won't get through before dark."

With our planting done, we went back to the house.

"It's a good thing Frank came out to help me, Liza, or I wouldn't have made it. When he gets a little bigger, I'd like to have him for my hired man."

Grandma agreed. "Now if you two will wash up, I'll get some fresh doughnuts to go with your glass of milk."

A few minutes later Grandpa lit his pipe and settled back in his chair. As he looked into the rising puffs of smoke his thoughts turned to other days and he spoke: "Back on the old farm I remember one spring I was out plowing a patch of ground, and wished we had more cleared land good enough for garden crops. As I stopped to rest the oxen, I looked up at the side of the mountain close by. The sidehill gougers were at home there and I could see where the ground had been stirred up by their sharp hoofs. It was much too steep to plow and plant. But it seemed too bad that a crop couldn't be grown in that good soil.

"As I went back to my plowing, I kept thinking there must be a way to plant that steep slope without climbing up there and taking a chance on falling off and getting hurt. All of a sudden I got an idea and headed back to the house leaving the oxen standing there.

"The first thing I did was to mix up a double handful of all the different kinds of garden seeds I could find.

Then I got my muzzle-loading shotgun and poured a charge of powder down the barrel. Next I rammed down a gun wad and poured in the mixed seeds and sealed them in place with another wad. Then I went outdoors and shot the whole kit and caboodle up into the side of the mountain. The seeds stuck in the soil, and as the days went by sprouted and grew and finally produced a crop. When the melons, pumpkins and the squashes got ripe they were so heavy they broke loose from the vines and just rolled down hill into the springy brush fence I had put at the bottom to catch them. But the root vegetables—the beets, carrots, turnips and radishes—they just stayed there in the ground and rotted."

"Why didn't you climb up and get them?"

"The slope was so steep that only a mountain-climber or a sidehill gouger could ever have gotten up there. But I kept thinking about it and after a couple of years of shotgun planting I finally figured out a way to harvest all of the crop. Every time I loaded the gun with seeds I put in some pole beans. When they grew they didn't have any poles to climb up on so they twisted in and out of the rows of carrots, beets, turnips and suchlike. Everything was so tangled up that when the pumpkins and squash were ripe and started to roll downhill, they hung onto the bean vines and the bean vines hung onto the tops of the root crops and pulled them right out of the ground. Everything in the garden ended up against my brush fence and all I had to do was to sort the vegetables out, load them in my box wagon and take them home.

"Shotgun farming gave us extra food without doing a lot of work. The neighbors soon took up the idea and every spring it sounded like the mountain people were a-feudin' when most everybody was out armed with a shotgun peppering the sides of the mountains with garden seeds."

Grandpa stood up, went to the stove and knocked the ashes out of his pipe. Grandma looked up and said: "Off to bed you go now, Frank. It's late and a growing boy needs lots of sleep."

Grandpa turned around with a twinkle in his eyes: "Frank, I've got a question to ask you before you go. You can think it over and give me your answer some other time. Which is heavier? A pound of lead or a pound of feathers? Now run along and sleep on it."

Snorka Birds

THERE WAS NO ONE IN GRANDMA'S KITCHEN ONE MILD evening late in May so I went into the parlor and looked out on the front porch. The light of a full moon outlined Grandma rocking slowly in her favorite chair with Grandpa sitting beside her puffing contentedly on his pipe. They were not talking, just sitting quietly looking at the big round yellow moon as it sailed through the clear sky above the sugar maple tree. I stepped out into the moonlight and shut the door quietly. "I wondered where you were."

"Hello, Frank," said Grandpa.

"Come on out and join us," added Grandma. "It's such a beautiful night we thought we'd sit out here for a while. It's cool enough for my shawl and there're no mosquitoes."

"I put the hammock up after supper," Grandpa commented in a low voice. "When I tied the rope to the corner post, a robin flew out of the grape vines. Then I noticed her nest in there with four blue eggs in it."

Grandma stopped rocking. "I hope she won't desert her nest, Abe. I'd like to watch her raise her family."

"She came back right away, Liza. She'll soon get used to us being so close. Now that it is dark, I don't think she'll get scared off if Frank uses the hammock."

I climbed in and pulled the tasseled sides over me. They felt good in the cool night air.

"We had a story in our reader at school today about birds. The ostrich lays the biggest egg and the hummingbird the smallest. It takes twenty-four hen's eggs to equal one ostrich egg."

Grandma laughed. "I wonder how long it would take to hard boil an ostrich egg for breakfast. A lot more than three minutes, I guess."

"There's a lot of difference in eggs," observed Grandpa. "In their size and also in their shape. I read once that some sea birds lay their eggs right on bare rocky ledges without any nest at all. They're pointed on one end so if they roll they'll go in a circle and not fall off."

"Too bad they don't have sense enough to lay eggs that are flat on one side," said Grandma quickly. "Then they'd have no trouble."

"That reminds me of the snorka bird that laid square eggs," Grandpa replied.

"I never heard of a snorka bird, Grandpa."

"Not many people have. I was lucky enough to get to see some."

"Tell me about it."

"I will if you think you can keep awake in the hammock. Several miles from where I lived on the old farm, there was a little-known spot called the Steenakill. It was a gloomy, spooky sort of place hardly ever visited by anyone. Some people said it was haunted. I once heard some old men talking about it at the blacksmith shop. They told me how to find it, so one nice spring day I decided to look into it. It turned out to be a narrow little valley hemmed in by steep rocky ledges, with a small stream running through it. The great tall trees looked big enough to be several hundred years old. They shut out most of the sunlight, and it was cool and peaceful underneath them.

"As I stood there quietly looking around, the stillness was suddenly broken by a high-pitched voice above my head that sounded as if it were yelling 'help! help!' It was a weird sound, something like the shrill cry of a peacock.

"I was nearly scared out of my wits. But I looked up in time to see a bird about the size of a pigeon fly backward from one tree to the next. The wind caught in its feathers, fluffing them out so it looked like an odd-shaped ball. Then another bird silently flew across but it was going head first and its feathers were neat and in place. Pretty soon a flock of birds like the first one was flying around, all going backward and filling the air with ear-splitting screams that almost made my hair stand on end. This was too much for my nerves, so I got out of there as fast as I could."

"What was the matter with them, Grandpa?"

"I didn't know then. In a few days I got over my fright and finally got up nerve enough to go back to see what it was all about. The screaming of the birds had stopped and all was peaceful. They were there, but silent. I could see them flying in pairs among the treetops, but now they all flew headfirst like ordinary birds do. Nothing happened to scare me that time so the next day I went back with a long rope. I tied one end to a stick and managed to throw it over the lower limb of one of the big trees. Then I climbed up. In nests lined with frog's hair, I found small, ivory-colored, square eggs in sets of odd numbers—three, five or seven."

"I never knew frogs had hair."

"They don't anymore, Frank. These birds picked it all off of them to line their nests with, so the frogs got discouraged and didn't grow hair anymore. Well, anyway, by this time I was so interested in these unusual birds that I visited them for several years and finally figured out what the whole thing was about.

"In the springtime the females were apparently in great pain when they were about to lay their square eggs. They flew backward as a sort of air-cooling measure to reduce their distress and screamed to show that their feelings were hurt.

"When you stop to think how happy a barnyard hen is when she lays her smooth rounded egg and cackles to let the world know how proud she is of what she's done, you can imagine how uncomfortable the snorka bird must have been laying and sitting on her six-sided ones. After the pain of egg-laying was over, the birds calmed down and flew about just like any other birds.

"When the time came for the eggs to hatch, it was dangerous to be in the Steenakill. The shells were so thick that the young birds could not get out by themselves, so the old birds took the eggs one at a time in their beaks and flew high in the air. Then they dropped

them on the rocks below to crack them open so the young could get out. They came down with the speed of bullets. The old birds then carried their chicks back to the nest to raise them."

"Do snorka birds still live in the Steenakill, Grandpa?"

"I wish I could say they do. When word of my find got around, some scientists came to see if the story was really true. A year later some young men came to stay at one of our summer boarding houses. They took long walks in the woods and climbed the mountains. They didn't say so, but we thought they belonged to some sort of club. Finally their vacation ended and they left. It wasn't until next spring that we found out what they had done. They had located the home of the snorka birds, climbed the trees and taken every egg. The old birds were so discouraged at having their nests robbed that they left the place and were never seen again.

"Many years later I found out who the young men were. One of the scientists who had come to see the birds was a professor who had taken a few of the square eggs to put in the school museum. When he showed them to his class and told the students the story, they came and gathered the eggs, polished them, put black dots of India ink on their six sides and used them for dice."

"Gee, Grandpa, that was a good story. Do you think you could tell the eggs from real dice?"

"I never had a chance to find out."

Grandma stood up. "We'd better go in before we get moonstruck. It's late for you to be up, Frank. Take a molasses cookie from the jar as you go through the pantry."

"And don't get any crumbs in bed," Grandpa added, "or the mice will be in with you."

High in the sky the man in the moon seemed to smile and wink his left eye, or was it a twig on the maple tree moving in the night wind?

Turtle Eggs

"I HAVE GOOD NEWS FOR YOU," I PROUDLY REPORTED TO Grandpa and Grandma as I walked into the kitchen. "Clifford and I found where Blackie stole her nest. It's under that pile of fence posts at the side of the barn."

"Good!" said Grandpa. "I hoped you two would find it. She was clucking around for a couple of days and then disappeared. How many eggs is she setting on?"

"I don't know. She wouldn't get off the nest. Clifford reached in and she pecked his hand and made it bleed. So we left her alone. We didn't want to scare her off because she might break some of the eggs."

"I'll have a look tomorrow. She is one of our best layers and any chicks she brings off should be as good. She reminds me of a hen we had many years ago that was always wanting to set."

Grandpa paused and reached for his pipe and tobacco jar on the shelf. Grandma used the delay to produce a loaf of freshly baked bread and cut off a thick slice. The butter dish and honey jar sat beside her on the table. A story and refreshments were in the making.

After a couple of puffs, Grandpa studied the rising smoke and said: "Mother love is a wonderful thing but some mothers carry it too far. Old Biddy was like that. She was a constant setter. If we took her eggs away from her, she would try to take over the nest of another hen. If she couldn't find eggs, she would set on anything that looked like them. One time I found her setting on a cigar box full of shiny white door knobs on my workbench in the barn. I figured I had no use for a brood of little porcelain door knobs, so I shooed her off and put the box on a high shelf where she couldn't get to it again.

"Another time she found a small puffball about the size of an egg growing close to the fence in the barnyard. She decided to try to hatch it. Now mushrooms grow fast in the darkness of a warm night, and this one was a giant puffball that might grow as big as a bushel basket. When daylight came the next morning, there was Old Biddy setting on the top of her 'egg', which was now nearly two feet in diameter."

"She must have looked funny, Grandpa, setting way up there."

"She did. Things like that kept happening all the time. Then one day I decided to play a joke on her. I came upon a big snapping turtle laying her eggs in a hole she had dug in a sandy spot at the edge of the pond. When she saw me, she quit and hurried back to water. I picked up twenty of the white, round, tough-shelled eggs and put them in a nest where Old Biddy would find them. Sure enough she took them over. Snapping turtle eggs take about three months to hatch. But she stayed with them and finally brought off a clutch of twenty little turtles. Much to my surprise they peeped like little chicks and had feathers on their heads and legs.

"Biddy was as proud of her new family as any hen could be. She tried her darndest to get them to eat the bugs she scratched up for them, but they wouldn't eat a thing. They kept heading toward the pond and finally got in the water. She almost drowned trying to herd them back to shore and ended up as mad as a wet hen could ever be. I guess that almost broke her heart. From that time on she lost all interest in setting and never again so much as clucked or laid another egg.

"Several years later I was dumbfounded to see a large snapping turtle with feathers on its head and legs come out of the pond and start to dig a hole in the sand. I hid in the bushes and watched her lay her eggs. After this was done, she pushed a mound of sand over them to hide them from sight, then stood up on top and proceeded to cackle like a hen."

Grandpa stood up, went to the stove, and knocked the ashes out of his pipe.

I broke the silence: "That was a good story, Grandpa. Now what if Blackie isn't setting on real eggs?"

"Don't worry about that hen," replied Grandma as she picked up my empty glass and plate. "She means business. I'll put a pan of water and some corn out for her so she won't have to hunt too far for something to eat. We don't want anything to happen to her nest.

"Now you'd better run along to bed. It's getting late."

Big Green Worms

GRANDMA WAS WASHING THE SUPPER DISHES WHEN I came into her kitchen one evening in July.

"Your favorite storyteller just went out in the garden to knock the potato bugs off the vines. Why don't you take this tin pail and get a broken shingle out in the woodshed and go help him?"

Armed with this equipment, I was welcomed by Grandpa as a big help.

"This stooping over is hard on my back. You're short enough to get close to them and besides your eyes are sharper than mine."

"There must be a lot of bugs here, Grandpa, from the looks of all the chewed leaves."

"Too many. I've been busy and forgot to keep an eye on 'em."

It was fun seeing the fat bugs bounce when they hit the bottom of the pail. The sound they made was a lot like big raindrops on a tin roof. We went through the potato patch in a hurry and soon had hundreds of the hard-shelled pests.

"Now to finish them off, Frank, we'll dump them all into an old tin pail, pour in a little kerosene and they'll kick the bucket in a hurry."

Our job finished, we returned to the kitchen.

"Liza," said Grandpa cheerfully, "if we don't have a good potato crop this year, it won't be Frank's fault. For every bug I found, I'll bet he got five."

"I think you two have earned a good rest. Why don't you go out and enjoy what little breeze there is on the front porch, and I'll make you some ice-cold lemonade to wet your whistles."

It was cooler out there but too warm to lie in the hammock so I sat on the floor.

"Catching potato bugs is fun, Grandpa. I'd like to help you again."

"I'll keep it in mind and call on you. Someday you may turn out to be the champion potato bug catcher of Ulster County."

Grandpa laughed and puffed contentedly on his pipe. "I wish all garden pests could be taken care of as easily as that. I'll never forget the trouble we had one year."

I turned around to face Grandpa. He was leaning back in his chair and seemed lost in thought as he looked toward the top of the maple tree at the edge of the front yard.

"First, somebody stole the salt block I had set out in the pasture for the cattle to lick. Then the early vegetables began to disappear out of the garden at night. Every morning I could see the places in the rows where the fattest beets, turnips, carrots and radishes had been pulled right out of the ground. And no tracks anywhere to tell what kind of thief was stealing them."

"Couldn't you do anything about it, Grandpa?"

"I had to. I knew if it kept up much longer the whole garden crop would be gone. So I took a horse blanket to lay on and spent the whole night hiding under the bushes close by. Nothing happened until daybreak. Then the branches high up in a tree at the edge of the garden began to shake and out crawled a flock of the biggest and ugliest green worms I ever hope to see. They didn't come down on the ground. Instead one worm sat up on its hind legs and spun out a long strand of silk. It was so light it blew across the garden and the end stuck to a tree on the other side. While the rest of the worms just set there in the treetops smacking their lips, the smallest one walked across the silk line like a circus performer on a tight wire and tied the end real tight so it couldn't pull loose. Then, one by one, they all crawled out on the tight cable and dropped another line right down onto the vegetables. Down they climbed into the garden. But instead of eating anything there, they pulled the plants out of the ground, shook off the dirt and carried them back along the cable and disappeared in the treetops. When the sun came up a few minutes later, the silk melted and was gone, leaving nothing behind to show what had gotten into the garden."

"Then what did you do?"

"The next morning I was out there at daybreak with my gun loaded with bird shot. When the first worms came into sight, I let them have it. But it didn't do any good. For every one I shot, it seemed as if two more took its place. Pretty soon I ran out of powder and lead, so I had to quit."

"Why didn't you get a club or something and go out in the garden after them?"

"I didn't dare. They were too big to fool around with and after all their bite might be poisonous. They looked like green monsters hanging by their tails and swinging on the ends of their silken ropes."

"What did you finally do?"

"Nothing. Your grandmother figured out a way to take care of 'em. She got some cayenne pepper and sprinkled it on the tops of the vegetables. Next morning when the worms came bright and early for their breakfasts, they sniffed, sneezed and snapped their heads off. And that ended the plague of the big green worms."

"Frank," Grandma's voice sounded from inside, "will you open the screen door for me so I won't spill the lemonade?"

I hurried to help her and seconds later we were enjoying a cool drink.

"You came just in time, Grandma. I just heard about the big worms in the garden and how you got rid of them with cayenne pepper."

Grandma smiled. "I've lived with your grandfather long enough to know that he has lots of stories about things I don't remember. Another thing I know and that is they grow with the telling."

Grandpa remained silent as he stood up and pushed his chair back. Evidently it was my bedtime. Then I remembered some unfinished business.

"Grandpa, did you ever find out who stole the cattle salt?"

"Yes, I did. The following October after the leaves

had fallen I found it wedged in a hole in the top of a big tree on the other side of the woods. The worms must have lugged it up there so they could salt the vegetables before eating them."

Boiler Episode

"Frank, will you get the fly swatter hanging from the nail over there and come sit at the table near me. There's a mosquito singing around here and it won't light. Your eyes are younger than mine. Maybe you can swat it."

"Where's Grandpa?"

"He went to the store to get some tobacco. He's been gone so long I suppose he's playing checkers down there with one of his cronies."

Just then we heard footsteps and Grandpa came in. "The mosquitoes are sure bad tonight," he said. "This warm rainy spell has brought 'em out in clouds. I bought a bottle of citronella to rub on in case they get too bad."

"There's a big one in here, Grandpa, and I'm trying to swat it before it gets after Grandma."

"I'll light my pipe and sit over there near you. Maybe my smoke'll get in its eyes and make 'em smart so it'll leave us alone."

"I hope Frank kills it," said Grandma. "We don't want it pestering us all night. I don't know why a pesky little thing that you can hardly see should bother a person so."

Grandpa looked at me and winked. "I take it this is just a regular size mosquito. When I came in, Frank said it was a big one. If it is and you'll show it to me, I'll club it with the broomstick and throw it out."

"Grandpa, I didn't say it was that big. You make it sound like a mosquito could be as big as a bird."

Grandma smiled. "If I don't miss my guess, there is a story brewing in your grandfather's head. You'd better pour yourself a glass of milk and get two oatmeal cookies from the jar. Then you can sit back and find out what your grandfather can come up with this time."

Back in my chair at the table, supplied with milk and cookies, I turned to Grandpa.

"You know, Frank, that quarrying is important work around here. Almost every day you see teamsters driving past with loads of bluestone. Well, one summer afternoon I was out in some rugged country trying to locate a ledge of bluestone to start a new quarry. I didn't have any luck and was on my way home when I came upon one that had been worked out. It was one I hadn't seen before so I was curious about it. Piles of broken rock and rubble were heaped up as high as small hills. The quarry hole itself where layers of stone had been taken out had filled up with water. Broken timbers lay scattered around, and off to one side stood an old rusty steam boiler that had been left behind when the stone had petered out."

"What was the boiler for, Grandpa?"

"It furnished steam power to operate the derricks to

lift the heavy slabs of stone up out of the hole. When it was in use, the boiler was like a big round hollow tank full of water with grates below where the fire burned to heat the water. I looked through the open door into the firebox and saw that the insides had all rusted away. While I was standing there, all at once I heard a loud angry humming noise. I looked up and there was a flock of the biggest mosquitoes I had ever seen swooping down at me from the top of a big pine tree. They looked as big as hawks. I knew at once I was in real trouble, so I dropped down on all fours and crawled inside the boiler and pulled the door shut just before they got to me. It was a close call, but at least I was safe. I could stay there all night if necessary, and maybe they'd go away when the sun came up. If they didn't, I'd be missed at home and a search party would certainly be sent out to find me.

"I could hear the bloodthirsty insects buzzing away outside and banging against the metal that separated us. Then pretty soon I heard a peculiar scraping sound and noticed a pinpoint of light right in front of me. The mosquitoes were so hungry they weren't going to wait for me to come out. One of them had drilled a hole right through the side of the boiler.

"I backed up and bumped into the sharp beak of another mosquito that had drilled through behind me, only a little lower down. Then I noticed little circles of light beginning to show all around me. The mosquitoes had spread themselves around the boiler and were boring through from all sides. The boiler was so narrow and their beaks were so long that some of them were bound to reach me.

"At that point I was really scared. If only a few of them punctured my skin, they could drain me dry of my life's blood. As I danced around trying to keep away from the beaks that were trying to find me, my foot hit something that rolled and clanked against the boiler. I bent my knees, squatted down in the darkness and reached around. My hand touched a length of iron from the rusted-out grate. I picked it up and stood upright. I was ready to fight back. Wherever I saw light coming through from the outside I hit the beak of a mosquito with a sidewise whack and bent it over so it couldn't be pulled out. I kept this up until I had clinched every single beak up against the side of the boiler. You should have heard the awful buzzing noise they made as they tried to get away. It sounded like a small sawmill.

"Now that I had fooled the mosquitoes, I figured that all I had to do was to kick the door open, crawl out and put them out of their misery by knocking them on the head with the length of iron. But all of a sudden the boiler began to rock and roll badly, and I had a terrible feeling of being seasick. I kicked the door open, hung my legs outside, and tried to reach the ground, but couldn't touch anything. Leaning back I looked through the open door toward the ground. All I saw was the tops of trees passing below me. The mosquitoes, frightened out of their wits at having their bills clinched to the boiler, had all flapped their wings and tried to escape. But they couldn't get loose, so away they flew carrying the boiler with them. They probably wanted to go back to their roost, wherever that was, but the weight of the boiler with me in it was too much for them. They only had enough mosquito-power to get off the ground and clear the tops of the trees and the rock ledges. We were slowly but surely dropping down into the valley below.

"I knew that I was again in great danger. If they were able to keep from falling into the mountainside and missed the little strip of flat land at the base, they'd be out over the Hudson River, which was a mile wide at that point. If they tried to fly across the river, they'd never make it and I'd likely be drowned inside the boiler. There was also another danger. A hunter might see this strange thing in the air and put a bullet into it, thinking it was a flying machine bringing invaders from Mars.

"Lucky for me the mosquitoes kept off the rocks and out of the trees while we were making this awful trip down into the valley. We finally made a crazy landing on a little level spot at the river's edge. The mosquitoes were completely tuckered out. I crawled out unhurt and legged it back up the mountain, leaving the mosquitoes to their fate.

"For some time after that, people said that a flock of big mosquitoes was seen flying about in the Catskills carrying a rusty old boiler along with them."

"Listen, Grandpa, I hear a humming noise now."

"I hear it, too," said Grandma. "It's that dratted mosquito that was so noisy before your grandfather came back from the store."

"I wonder why it's been so quiet, Grandma?"

"It was probably listening to your grandfather's story."

"There it goes now." Grandpa pointed across the table. A big mosquito was flying slowly upward toward the wall. Its body was swollen amost to the bursting point with blood.

I grabbed the fly swatter and took a mighty swipe at it. There was the crash of broken glass as the kerosene lamp chimney was smashed to pieces and we were in darkness.

There was a deep silence.

A light flared as Grandpa scratched a smelly slow-burning, sulphur match and walked across the room to the wall lamp near the stove. He came back with it in his hand and set it on the table. On one of the broken pieces of lamp chimney was a big splotch of blood.

After my soft, "I'm sorry," Grandma leaned over and patted my head. "I'll get a new chimney tomorrow with my egg money. I asked you to swat the mosquito and you did!"

Mosquitoes Invade
the Cabin

GRANDMA LOOKED UP FROM HER SEWING. "COME IN Frank, your grandfather just went out to the pump to fetch a pail of water. If the mosquitoes don't carry him off, he'll be back in a couple of minutes."

"Are they that bad tonight, Grandma? I hope they aren't the big ones that carried him away in the boiler that time."

"If they were, I'm afraid screen doors and mosquito netting wouldn't keep them out. Here he comes now."

The door opened and Grandpa carried the water over to the small table in the corner. Taking the tin dipper from the nail, he quenched his thirst and asked, "Who wants a nice cool drink?"

First Grandma, then I drank from the dipper.

Seating himself, Grandpa turned to me. "The mosquitoes are out in full force tonight. From the way they puncture your skin, I sometimes wonder if they can be part woodpecker." He smiled and reached for his pipe.

"Do you know any more good mosquito stories, Grandpa?"

He nodded his head, lit his pipe, then sat quietly

for a minute as if to bring together his thoughts.

"When your grandmother and I were first married, we lived for a while in a little old log cabin on my father's farm. In those days cabins didn't have locks and keys. The door was kept shut by means of a wooden bar or latch that fitted into a slot on the inside. This could be lifted from the outside by pulling on the latch-string that hung out through a small hole in the door. All you had to do to lock up at night was to pull the latch-string in."

"That was easy, and you didn't have any keys to lose."

"Yes, it was very simple. Well, one summer we had a long rainy season and the mosquitoes were unusually bad. One night we were scared by the sound of the door opening with a bang. I jumped out of bed, shut it, and started to crawl back in when something lit on my head. As I reached up to grab it, it slipped through my fingers and got away. Stumbling around in the pitch black darkness I finally found a match and lit a couple of candles. By the dim light I made out several creatures flying around the room. From their long legs and beaks and smooth, gray wings I knew they were big mosquitoes. I set the candles on the table, grabbed up the broom and tried to hit them, but they were too quick for me.

"I told your grandmother to stay covered up in bed. My first thought was to load the shotgun and blast them, but this would have ruined the inside of the cabin so I gave up that idea. Yet somehow I had to destroy them. Mosquitoes as big as birds were dangerous and I didn't want to open the door and let them get away. We talked it over and finally decided on a plan.

"Your grandmother got up and took the broom while I lit two more candles. Holding one in each hand, I went over and stood in one corner of the room. She kept chasing them until one flew into my corner. Reaching up quickly I singed its wings in the flames and it fell to the floor where I stomped on it. We kept this up until we had all except one, which flew around so fast we couldn't corner it. Finally when the candles had almost burned down to my fingers, it perched on the mantle to get its breath. Just as I rushed up to burn its wings, it turned its head and blew the candles out. At the same time the door opened again and our night visitor got away."

"Golly, Grandpa, what made the door open?"

"I forgot to pull the latch-string in before we went to bed. Sometime in the night a flock of these oversize mosquitoes had begun to prowl around the cabin. One of them must have lit on the latch-string and its weight was enough to lift the latch on the inside. One of them stayed on guard on the outside and it finally opened the door again and let the last one out."

"What did you do with all the dead mosquitoes?"

"I threw them outdoors, and the next day I nailed them on the side of the barn as a warning to the others.

"One day the following spring when I was tapping the maple trees I noticed that the bodies were still there and that the long, hollow beaks were weathered and gray but still as hard as horn. I sawed them off and drove them into the auger holes for spiles to hang the buckets on to catch the sap. They were much better than wooden ones and lasted for many years."

"I'm glad you found some use for those mosquitoes, Grandpa, after all the trouble you had with them. If you ever kill another big one, why don't you saw off its beak and use it for the stem of the corncob you're smoking? That one looks pretty well chewed up."

Grandpa looked at me in surprise. "By Jove, that's a good idea. I'll keep it in mind."

"Abe," Grandma said, laughing, "I told you he's going to be a chip off the old block. I see now what you meant when you said storytelling was good for the imagination.

"Now, I think it's getting late and you'd better quit for the night. Do you want something to eat, Frank, before you go?"

"Not tonight, thank you, Grandma. It's so hot I'm not hungry. I'd like another drink of water though. It's so good and cold."

"It should be," said Grandpa, "it came from the north side of the well."

Pet Goldfish

"Your grandfather said he'd be late getting back tonight", said Grandma. "He's been gone all day, driving a drummer up through Woodstock and around to Shokan with stops at all the country stores along the way. He must be taking a lot of orders to need this much time."

"Why do they call the man a drummer, Grandma? Does he carry a drum?"

"No, I guess a salesman is called a drummer because he travels around and drums up trade for his firm. Some firms don't have drummers. They send out a catalog and you order what you want from it and they ship it to you."

"You mean like your Sears-Roebuck catalog?"

"Yes. Maybe you'd like to look at it while we wait for your grandfather."

I opened up the heavy book. Its 1120 pages listed everything from absorbent cotton to zithers and there was a picture of most of the thousands of items mentioned.

"Why, Grandma, it'd take hours to look through all these pages."

"Yes, I guess it would. Wait a minute! I think that must be your grandfather coming up the steps. You go right on looking at the catalog while he eats his supper. I hope it isn't spoiled waiting for him."

Grandpa came in. "We had a long hard trip. I fed and bedded Nell down for the night before I came up to the house. That mare certainly earned her keep today."

"Where's the drummer, Grandpa?"

"He's staying at Lane's hotel. Tomorrow he takes the train back to Kingston. After he works his territory, he goes back to New York City."

"Did you ever go to New York City?"

"I think you'd better let your grandfather eat his supper first, Frank. After he's through you can visit."

I had looked at pictures of hundreds of things in the catalog—toys, baseball mitts, bicycles, wagons and many more—before Grandpa pushed back from the table, lit his pipe and sat himself comfortably in his armchair.

"Visiting with Mr. Treadwell, the drummer, between stores reminded me of the time I thought New York City was the answer to all my dreams. From the stories I'd read, life there seemed to be full of excitement and good times with plenty of interesting work and big pay. Since I wasn't twenty-one, I kept begging my folks for permission to go until at last they gave in. So off I went to the Big City to win fame and fortune."

"I'll bet you were excited."

"Yes, I was. I got a place to stay in a rooming house

and then started out to look for a job. After walking around for a few hours, I finally saw a sign: 'Help Wanted' in the office of a lumber company. I went in and asked for the job which turned out to be piling and loading lumber. Being big and strong, I was hired.

"I liked the work but as the days passed I found that I wasn't happy. I was too lonesome. The men I worked with were friendly enough, but at quitting time they went home to their families. The people in the rooming house had their own friends. No one paid any attention to a country boy.

"Then one day I found a friend. I was walking along the streets killing time by looking in store windows when I saw a pet shop. In the window were live dogs, cats and monkeys. I thought it would be nice to have one but I knew the landlady would object. A tank of goldfish sat beside the cages. And there, I realized, was something that wouldn't need much care and yet would be company for me at night and on weekends when I spent a lot of time in my room. So I went in and bought a bowl and one large goldfish.

"After that it was more fun to come home at night. And after a time the goldfish seemed glad to see me, too. It would come to the surface to have its back scratched and stick its head out of the water to nip my finger.

"As the days passed, the goldfish became so tame it would jump out of the bowl when it heard the key turn in the lock and wriggle across the floor to meet me. I'd put it back in the water and pretty soon it would jump out again and tag along at my heels.

Finally it spent more time out of water than in, so I always had to be careful not to step on it. Just for fun, I taught it to sit up and beg for food, to roll over and also to shake hands . . . I mean fins."

"I wish I could have seen your trained goldfish. Did you have it a long time?"

"Yes, I kept it for months. Between my pet goldfish and the park across the street, I took to city life pretty well. I spent a lot of time in the park because the pond and the little stream that ran into it, the trees, birds and squirrels all reminded me of the Catskills and I was happy there. I liked best to walk there bright and early on Sunday mornings before the rest of the people were up.

"One Sunday morning I got the idea that perhaps the goldfish would like to go to the park with me. So I made a little harness for it from a shoelace, carried it across the street, fixed a leash to the harness and the two of us slowly strolled about. If anyone came along, I hid it under my coat because I didn't want people to think I was queer walking my goldfish on a leash. For many Sundays the fish enjoyed these outings with me. It snapped up flies that came near it and several times when birds sang in the trees overhead, it opened its mouth and made a hissing noise as if it were trying to sing.

"Many times when no one was in sight, I took off the harness and let the goldfish roll and romp in the dew on the grass like a frisky puppy. It enjoyed its freedom so much that I finally got careless, and one day I left the harness off as we were crossing the rustic foot bridge. The goldfish slipped through a wide crack in the flooring and fell into the water below where it drowned before I could fish it out.

"That was the turning point in my life because I was so broken-hearted I lost all interest in living in the city anymore. A week later I was back in the Catskills to stay."

"I'm sorry your goldfish drowned, Grandpa, but I'm glad you came back here to live or I might never have met you."

Grandma smiled and spoke: "I'm glad he came back, too. Maybe someday you'll have a pet goldfish, Frank. Then your grandfather can help you teach it some of those tricks. We'll talk about it some other time because right now you should be on your way to bed."

As I started to go, Grandpa had an afterthought. "Don't ever trade Tiger in for a trained goldfish. Your cat is smarter and makes a much better pet."

Indian Story

I COULD HARDLY WAIT TO TELL THE GOOD NEWS. IN OUR two-room country school we now had a small shelf of three-dozen brand new books.

"The teacher says the school board bought them and she'll read stories to us, and sometimes if our lessons are done and we get good marks, we can sit right there in school and read them, too."

There was no public library in our small mountain village, and Grandpa and Grandma agreed that the new bookshelf was a wonderful thing.

"What are the books about?" Grandma asked.

"Miss Smith said they're different from school books. They tell about animals and people and history and adventure and things like that. She read us one story before school was let out. It was about a man named John Coulter and how he escaped from the Indians out west. It sure was exciting."

Grandpa turned his armchair around. "I don't think I've heard that one. Why don't you tell us about it, Frank."

"That's a good idea, Abe," Grandma nodded in agreement. "I'd like to hear it, too."

I took a deep breath and began.

"A long time ago we didn't have any railroads across the country. People didn't know what the Far West looked like. So the government sent some men out to see. They called it an expedition, and it was headed by two men who were told to go up the Missouri River and cross the mountains into Oregon."

"Do you remember their names?" Grandpa asked.

"The teacher said it was the Lewis and Clark expedition, so I guess that's who they were. On their way back one of the men asked if he could stop and catch some beaver, and the rest went on without him. His name was John Coulter. He had good luck and thought about all the money he would get when he sold the furs at a trading post.

"Then one day the Indians caught him. He was scared, but he acted very calm. They made him run between two rows of young braves, and they started to hit him with sticks and clubs. He grabbed one of their clubs and hit them right and left. The old Indians laughed to see the young men knocked down.

"Next the chiefs decided to burn him at the stake. They told him this in sign language, and he laughed at them as though this would be fun. They didn't like this so they tried to figure out a better way to hurt him. Finally they asked him if he was a good runner. He said no. So they told him they would have a race. The young braves would take their spears and chase him and see who could hit him first. Then they took all of his clothes off and turned him loose on the open prairie. It was flat country, and he couldn't hide."

"Do you mean he was completely naked and even barefooted!" exclaimed Grandma in alarm.

"I guess so. He must have been tough. He really was a good runner and he was so scared that he ran like the wind. He ran so hard that his nose started to bleed. But he did keep so far ahead of the Indian runners that they didn't have a chance to throw a spear into his back.

"Miles away he could see some trees. In the prairie country this meant water was there. He ran toward the trees. Finally he got tired and slowed down, but the Indians got tired too and most of them were a long ways behind. At last he could hear the sound of only one Indian following him. But even though he might be hit in the back any minute by a spear, he could not run another step. So he stopped and turned around. The Indian behind him was so surprised to see the front of the white man covered with blood that he thought he must have been chasing some kind of evil spirit. He stubbed his toe and fell and broke his spear. I guess that knocked the wind out of him because he couldn't get up. When the rest of the Indians saw what had happened, they started to run faster. But John Coulter was now so far ahead they couldn't catch him.

"He turned and headed again for the trees. When he got there, he found a river with some rocks sticking up in it. Trees and brush had caught on the rocks. He jumped into the water and swam to them. Then he dove down and came up with his head hidden under the brush so he could breathe and not be seen.

"Pretty soon the Indians came down the bank. They saw where the tracks ended at the edge of the water. They looked up and down the bank on both sides of the river. They swam out to the rocks and walked on the brush over his head but they couldn't find him. Finally it got dark, and they went away.

"He floated downstream all night and was careful not to touch the shore. He knew the Indians would be back in the morning to look for his tracks. He hid on a little island when it grew light the next day, and then floated down the river again the second night. By this time he was far enough away from the Indians so he went ashore. He was a good woodsman and made his way across the country like a wild animal without any clothes, finding enough to eat to keep him alive. It was cold weather, too. It's a wonder he didn't freeze to death. He went on like this for nearly three hundred miles. Many days later he came to a trading post and told this story."

Grandpa beamed: "That was a good story, Frank, and well told too. It was all new to me."

"I can see that we're going to have another story-teller in the family," Grandma added with a smile.

She got up and went to the sliding panel that opened into the shaft where the dumbwaiter was suspended. When she pulled down on the rope that hung in the opening, a shelf filled with good things to eat came up from the cool, dark cellar below.

"I'm glad you both liked my story. Don't you know any about Indians, Grandpa?"

He gently stroked his chin-whiskers. "The early

settlers around here had their troubles with the Indians too from time to time. I'll have to put on my thinking cap and some other night see if I can come up with an Indian story as good as yours."

Grandma motioned toward the table. "Frank, you'd better get busy. It's late and past your bedtime. I hope you won't have a nightmare and roll out of bed trying to escape from the Indians."

We all laughed.

Tom Quick

"GRANDPA, IS YOUR STORY TONIGHT ABOUT INDIANS? You were going to try to think up one."

"Sort of. It's about a man who had so many narrow escapes from the Indians they'd fill a book. I'll tell you just a few of them tonight."

"What was his name and did he live right around here?"

"His name was Tom Quick, and he was born in the southern part of Ulster County not many miles from here. While he was still a boy, his family moved a few miles over the state line into Pennsylvania and settled near Milford. A short time after that his father was killed in an Indian uprising.

"Tom grew to be a strong, tall, quiet man who became noted as a hunter of Indians as well as wild animals. He roamed all over this part of the state. He could speak the Indian tongue and was as much at home in the woods as any Indian. They made many attempts to take his life but missed their mark so often they finally believed he led a charmed life and couldn't be hit by an Indian's bullet. So they decided that the only way to get rid of him was to capture him alive and then figure out how to dispose of him.

"He had many narrow escapes. One night an Indian climbed into Tom's pig-pen and held a squealing pig between his knees, hoping Tom would think a bear had caught it and rush out so the rest of the Indians could capture him. Right away Tom knew a bear wouldn't let the pig squeal that long before killing it. Another time three Indians drove Tom's cow deep into the woods. It had a bell on it so Tom could locate it and drive it into the barn at night where it would be safe from bears and wolves. The Indians took the bell and rang it so they could lure Tom into an ambush and catch him. He wasn't fooled because the Indians didn't ring the bell the way the cow did."

"You make it sound like some kind of game they were playing, Grandpa."

"In this game a man's life was at stake. And Tom was smart enough or lucky enough to outwit them."

"Then the Indians never did catch Tom?"

"Oh, yes, they did. One time he was sitting in one of his cabins on the top of a mountain eating his dinner. Suddenly without warning three strapping big Indians rushed in and knocked him down. They looked around and in one corner saw an empty barrel with the loose head for it leaning against the wall. One of the Indians rolled it outside. Then they stuffed him into the barrel and pounded the head back in so he couldn't get out."

"Why did they put Tom in the barrel, Grandpa?"

"He heard them say they were going to roll him off the mountain where it dropped down a thousand

feet onto some rocks below. But first they were going back to camp to get the rest of their hunting party to see the fun.

"Pretty soon the Indians went away and all was quiet. Tom tried his best to force the barrel head loose, but it wouldn't budge. Doubled up in his tight coop, he didn't have a ghost of a chance of getting out. How long, he wondered, before they would come back and send him rolling to his death?

"After a while he heard a little noise. Something was stirring just outside. The bung was out of the side of the barrel and a beam of light shone in. Tom scrooched down and managed to put his eye to the hole. A big hungry-looking panther had found the haunch of bear meat Tom had been eating and was tearing into it.

"But before it had a chance to swallow the first mouthful, there was a terrible scream and a second panther came into view. Right then and there started the biggest cat fight you can imagine. The air was filled with yowling and hissing and flying fur, as the two animals clawed and bit each other and tore up the ground. The pitched battle went on for some time as the two evenly matched cats fought tooth and nail. There wasn't a thing Tom could do doubled up inside, although several times they bumped the barrel and almost tipped it over.

"Suddenly the shaft of light coming in through the bung hole was shut off, and something furry and ticklish brushed Tom's face. He grabbed on with both hands and found he had hold of the end of a panther's tail. Just for want of anything else to do, he gave it a twist. There followed such a screech outside that Tom's hair stood on end. The tail pulled tight, and Tom hung on for dear life. The barrel tipped over and started to slide, then bump and finally seemed to be in the air part of the time as the cat ran faster and faster.

"How long this went on, you'll have to guess. But it ended suddenly with a crash as the barrel seemed to explode and Tom was out, free and unhurt. Bumping a boulder had done the trick. And there at his feet lay the panther scared to death, its fur turned snow white from its terrible fright."

"Golly, Grandpa, my heart is pounding like it happened to me."

"Frank, your grandfather has me about worn out, too. How long is Tom Quick going to keep this up with the Indians, Abe?"

"According to the story they never did do away with him. He died an old man, in bed, from smallpox."

Special Delivery

"I've a story for you tonight, Frank, that's a little bit different. It's about Hank Smith and Ezekiel Axenhammer's daughter whose name was Rose. I hope you'll like it."

Grandpa paused while Grandma removed the lamp chimney and skillfully trimmed the smoking wick with her small-bladed scissors. As she returned to her low rocking chair, he continued:

"Hank was a quiet, shy, tenderhearted boy who didn't like the idea of killing things. He'd never shot a bear or deer or trapped a muskrat. His father couldn't get him to stick a pig at butchering time, and he wouldn't even cut off the head of a chicken for a Sunday dinner. He was happiest when he was working alone in the woods, felling shingle trees and splitting the clear logs into thousands of neat shingles.

"Zeke Axenhammer's cabin stood in a sizeable clearing right at the foot of a steep mountain. His wife died when Rose was born and the neighbors had pitched in and helped him raise the baby. At eighteen Rose was a fine young woman and a good housekeeper for her father.

"Hank and Rose knew each other, but they were so shy they had hardly much more than passed the time of day. This was all changed when a bear ran across the road late one afternoon as Rose was driving home alone from the village. The horse reared up and took to the ditch, and Rose rolled out into the mud and water. Hank was up the road a piece and caught the runaway. He turned the wagon around and went back and found that Rose wasn't hurt. From then on they took a liking to each other.

"As the days went by, Zeke began to notice that Hank passed the cabin quite often and somehow Rose always happened to be outside about that time and they would stand and talk over the front gate.

"Now Zeke was strong and tough and had hunted and trapped all his life and wasn't afraid to tackle a bear or panther armed only with an ax or a hunting knife. He'd been known to kill a wounded bear with a club. He was a bad-tempered man, especially if he thought somebody might want to marry his **daughter** and break up his home. And of the many people he didn't like, Hank Smith headed the list because he was so different.

"Zeke began to worry that he might lose Rose, and the more he worried the meaner he got. Finally he told her he noticed the Smith boy hanging around and asked if she wanted to marry him. Rose said she did, and that Hank had asked her. Nothing more was said. Zeke didn't want to hurt his daughter. But he hoped to work out a scheme to break up their plans.

"The next time he saw them together, he asked

Hank if he'd ever shot a deer or a bear; if he'd ever trapped a panther or a wolf. Of course Hank hadn't. Had he ever caught any wild game? Yes, once he set out some snares for rabbits.

"Zeke was getting madder and madder, and finally he decided there was no use beating around the bush any longer so he said: 'Hank, in spite of all this, I understand you want to marry my daughter?'

"Hank was so scared he wanted to run. He turned red as a beet, looked at the ground and stammered: 'Wh-w-why, I've had it in mind, but I never did get around to ask you for her hand.'

"Zeke forced himself to smile: 'Prove to me you're a man,' he said, 'by bringing me in a bear and you can have her.'

"Hank took a deep breath of relief and turned to go. 'I'll get you a bear if it's the last thing I ever do!'

"Before Hank got away very far, Zeke called him back: 'You understand it's got to be a real live bear? I don't want you to bring me a dead secondhand one you got from somebody else.'

"Hank's heart fell into his boots. That was Zeke's way of telling him he couldn't have his daughter. He turned and went away and never came back to see Rose anymore."

"Oh, Grandpa, wasn't there any way to make Rose's father change his mind?"

"No. Zeke Axenhammer was a tough customer and nobody wanted to tangle with him. After that Hank kept more and more to himself. Every day, come rain or shine, it looked like he was trying to forget Rose by working himself to death.

"It got to be winter, but Hank never let up. One cold day he was up on top of the mountain above the village looking for shingle trees. The snow was waist-deep but covered with a hard crust so it held his weight. He found a good straight tree and started to chop it down. While he was working at it, a bear in the hollow tree next to him crawled out to see what the racket was all about. It stood up on its hind legs and walked closer. Hank raised his ax for another cut, heard a noise and turned to see the bear almost upon him. He swung at the bear, and the next second the ax went sailing through the air. Bears are good boxers and this one knocked the ax twenty feet away. The bear closed in and grabbed Hank in its powerful arms. A man caught in a bear hug can be squeezed to death in a hurry. As they rasseled each other around on the slippery crust, their feet went out from under them and they started to slide down the mountain, with the bear on its back still holding Hank in its arms. Faster and faster they went, somehow missing stumps and stones. At the foot of the mountain the going was smoother. Hank raised his head up enough from the bear's chest to see that they had hit a logging road. They coasted along it a mile or so until it made a sharp turn and they went whipping back into the brush. By this time they were going so fast, they went up a sharp ridge and down the other side into the village below.

"Suddenly there was a terrific crash and a building fell down around them. The bear crawled a few feet

to one side and sat up. Hank stood up in the midst of broken furniture, loose shingles and a mess of kitchen ware. A third creature groaned and crawled out of the pile of wreckage.

"What hit us?" it said, "a tornado or an earthquake?"

"Hank rubbed his eyes. It was Zeke Axenhammer!

'Why it's me,' shouted Hank as he pulled Zeke to his feet. 'I brought you that live bear you wanted. Thought I'd surprise you so I came in without knocking.

'Where's Rose? We're going to get married!'

Going Away

GRANDMA WAS SITTING ALONE AT THE KITCHEN TABLE reading her Bible as I entered through the pantry door. She looked up and turned toward me. Her usual smile was missing.

"I'm glad you came in, Frank. It's lonesome tonight without your grandfather, and that chirping cricket over there in the woodbox is making me nervous. Seems like it's telling me another winter will soon be here."

"Grandma, is it really true that you and Grandpa are going to move away soon?"

"Yes, it is, I'm sorry to say. Now that New York City has bought all the land around here and is going to build dikes and fill the valley with water, it's just a matter of time before everybody will have to move out. Your grandfather and I are getting along in years and we think we'd better move now before all the workmen come to build the dam."

"Why did they have to come here? Why didn't they go some other place?"

"The city has grown so big they need more water. Their engineers made a survey and decided this part

of the Catskills was the best place to get it. They'll
run a big pipe line from the dam all the way down to
New York so they'll always have a good supply of pure
mountain water."

"Where's Grandpa tonight?"

"He took the train to Kingston and then went out
from there to the village of Hurley to buy a house.
There'll be land enough for a garden and some flowers, and a small barn for a horse and buggy. We'll keep
a few chickens.

"It's a nice quiet village, and we think we'll be happy
there for whatever time we have left. It won't be easy
to go."

"Gee whiz! If you move away, I won't see you again
or hear any more of Grandpa's stories."

"It won't be quite that bad. I hope you'll come and
see us once in a while. You're just at the right age
where you two belong together. An old man needs
attention. He needs to be wanted. And in you he sees
our Willie again, growing up healthy and strong."

"Who was Willie?"

"He was your father's little brother. When he was
about as big as you are now, he caught a bad cold one
winter. It turned into pneumonia, and we lost him."

"Gee, Grandma, I'm sorry about that."

"That's why your grandfather likes to tell you his
stories and answer your questions."

"After you and Grandpa go away and this side of
the house is empty, I won't want to come in here anymore. It'll make me sad. Do you think somebody else
will move in?"

"No, Frank. No one else will move here. Instead all of the families will move away, the buildings will be torn down and all of the trees and bushes will be cut. Then everything will be burned over and the whole valley filled with water."

"It scares me, Grandma, to think that some day all the things we see around here will be gone and the whole place will be covered with water."

"It frightens all of us, Frank, but we can't do anything about it. In years to come when people look at the beautiful lake that'll be made here, the old village and the old ways will be forgotten. Only the mountains will be the same."

"I wonder where we'll live then?"

"I think your folks plan to move to Kingston so you and your brother and sister can go to high school."

"I'll be afraid to live in a city. Grandpa took me there on the train one day. They have buildings three stories high and street cars pulled by horses and electric lights they can turn on at night and policemen walking around in blue suits with brass buttons and carrying clubs. I didn't see any boys with bare feet. I'll bet they make 'em dress up all the time like it was Sunday."

When Grandma stopped laughing, she said, "You'll learn to like it there. Besides, Hurley will be only three miles away from you then. During school vacations you can come out and stay with us and go barefoot all you want to."

Grandma got up and brought me a glass of milk and two oatmeal cookies. Somehow I wasn't hungry. While

I ate in silence, she turned to her Bible again and seemed to be reading. Even so she was aware of me and when I had finished she looked up and said, "It's getting late now and high time you were on your way to bed. I'm glad you came in to keep me company. I plumb forgot about the cricket."

"Thank you, Grandma, and goodnight. And even if other people forget, I'll never forget you and Grandpa and all the fun we had here."

"We have had many nice evenings together, haven't we? I hope you will remember your grandfather's tall tales and tell them to your children and grandchildren. And someday you might even put them in a book so they'll never be forgotten."

I went quietly back through the door at the end of the pantry and upstairs to bed. For a long time I lay there looking out at the shimmering stars as they hung high above the dark outline of the mountains.

Someday I might!